Royal Greenwich Observatory

An Historical Review issued on the occasion of its Tercentenary

William Hunter McCrea FRS

LONDON HER MAJESTY'S STATIONERY OFFICE 1975

© *Crown copyright 1975*
ISBN 0 11 880616 5

Printed in England for Her Majesty's Stationery Office
by Burrup, Mathieson & Co, Ltd.   Dd 288357K

Contents

Illustrations

Plate 1 Greenwich
Flamsteed's Sextant 1676 (replica)
Halley's 8-foot Quadrant 1725
Pond's 10-foot Transit Instrument 1816
in Bradley Transit Room 1750
Airy's Transit Circle 1851
defining Prime Meridian
Photographs: Woodmansterne Ltd.,
Watford

Plate 2 Greenwich
Flamsteed House (1675/6) from
Greenwich Park
Old Greenwich Observatory, Meridian
Building
Photographs: Woodmansterne Ltd.,
Watford
'Physical Observatory' 1891–9
Plates 1 and 2, all photographs published
by National Maritime Museum

Plate 3 Herstmonceux
Herstmonceux Castle (*c.* 1446) from
south-west
Castle from north and Isaac Newton
Telescope
Equatorial Group of Telescopes:
three of the six domes
Royal Arms of the House of Stuart on
Equatorial Group
Photographs: David Calvert, Royal
Greenwich Observatory
Castle and grounds
Photograph: Aerofilms Ltd.

Plate 4 Herstmonceux
Isaac Newton and Equatorial Telescope
domes
Photograph: Aerofilms Ltd.
Thompson 30-inch reflector
Isaac Newton Telescope:
Cassegrain spectrograph
Isaac Newton Telescope:
coudé spectrograph
Photographs: David Calvert, Royal
Greenwich Observatory

Plate 5 Astronomers Royal
John Flamsteed 1675–1719
Edmond Halley 1720–42
James Bradley 1742–62
Nathaniel Bliss 1762–4
Nevil Maskelyne 1765–1811
John Pond 1811–35
Sir George Biddell Airy 1835–81
Sir William Henry Mahoney Christie
1881–1910
Sir Frank Watson Dyson 1910–33
Sir Harold Spencer Jones 1933–55
Sir Richard van der Riet Woolley
1956–71
Portrait of Flamsteed lent by Royal
Society to National Portrait Gallery
Portrait of Bliss by courtesy of
Mr. M. L. Dix Hamilton

Plate 6
Directors
E. Margaret Burbidge 1972–3
Alan Hunter, 1973–5
F. Graham Smith, from 1976
Annual Visitation 1897
from left R. B. Clifton, A. W. Rücker,
H. H. Turner, Sir G. G. Stokes,
W. D. Barber (Sec.), Lord Rayleigh,
J. W. L. Glaisher, (Sir) G. H. Darwin,
Lord Rosse, A. A. Common,
Sir W. Huggins, (Sir) F. W. Dyson
(Chief Assistant)
250th Anniversary, 1925
H.M. King George V with the President
of the Royal Society (Sir Charles
Sherrington) on 26 July 1925

Plate 7 Greenwich
Airy's Altazimuth 1847
Great Equatorial 1859 with 12¾-inch
object glass by Merz
Magnetic Pavilion about 1890
'Onion dome' with 28-inch refractor
1894

Plate 8   Herstmonceux: Spencer Jones group
Reversible Transit Circle:
Greenwich 1936, Herstmonceux 1957
Photographic Zenith Tube 1955
Danjon Astrolabe 1960
Spencer Jones Pavilions
from left: Astrolabe, RTC, PZT
Photographs: David Calvert, Royal
Greenwich Observatory

Plate 9   Herstmonceux
Photoheliograph (further large tube and
camera) for daily photograph of Sun's
disk, and observer viewing Sun through
Lyot filter
Astrographic 13-inch refractor
Thompson 26-inch refractor, with
Merz $12\frac{3}{4}$-inch refractor as guider
Yapp 36-inch reflector with image tube
spectrograph

Plate 10   Herstmonceux: West Building
Building containing Nautical Almanac
Office, Time department, Computer,
and other departments
Part of Time department
GALAXY measuring machine in
Astrometric department
Spectrograph constructed in
Instrumentation and Engineering
division for Anglo-Australian 150-inch
telescope
Photographs: All plates 9, 10 except
photoheliograph, David Calvert, Royal
Greenwich Observatory

Plate 11   Herstmonceux: Isaac Newton Telescope
H.M. the Queen with full-scale replica
of Newton's own reflecting telescope of
1671 (*'Bexhill-on-Sea Observer'*)
H.M. the Queen with Astronomer Royal
at inauguration 1 December 1967
(*'Evening Argus'*, Brighton)
Isaac Newton Telescope (INT)
Photograph: David Calvert, Royal
Greenwich Observatory

Plate 12   Royal Greenwich Observatory
Sunspots during International
Geophysical Year: one of daily
photographs from photoheliograph
1 April 1958
Globular cluster of stars M3
(INT photograph)
Spiral galaxy M51 (INT photograph)
Irregular galaxy M82 (INT photograph)

Acknowledgements

I thank Dr Alan Hunter, Director of the Royal Greenwich Observatory, Herstmonceux, for the facilities and hospitality of the Observatory that I have been privileged to enjoy while writing this account. I thank his colleagues who have helped in so many ways.

Mr Philip Stevenson Laurie, Head of the Solar Department and Archivist, has with unexampled generosity placed his superb knowledge of the Observatory's history and of its records at my disposal. Without this the account could not have been compiled.

I thank Mr David Calvert of the Solar and Photographic Departments for making and providing most of the illustrations, and Miss Anita Hewerdine, Miss Janice Gaydon and Miss Hazel Simmons for their work on the typescript. I wish to thank others who have allowed me to reproduce photographs in accordance with the printed acknowledgements.

Lt-Cdr H. D. Howse RN has given me valuable information about the buildings and instruments at Greenwich for which I am most grateful.

The work has been done during my tenure of a Leverhulme Emeritus Fellowship; I record my gratitude to the Leverhulme Trust.

Her Majesty's Stationery Office and the Printers have applied their outstanding skills to the production; it is a pleasure to acknowledge my indebtedness.

The selection of material to be included and comments thereon have been my responsibility.

W. H. McCrea
1 July 1974

Vista

King Charles II founded his Observatory for the practical purpose of accurate navigation out of sight of land. The mariner on a featureless ocean had nothing to help him except the sky – Sun, Moon, planets and stars. Any accurate observation had to involve the stellar background. The first need therefore was precise knowledge of the positions of the 'fixed' stars. In getting this, any known motion of the Earth's axis had to be allowed for, and so any relevant constant – in the first place the constant of precession – had to be determined or corrected. But as information increases in scope and accuracy, more phenomena become apparent, and still more observations become necessary in order to take them into account. There are refraction by the Earth's atmosphere, further motions of the Earth's axis, the proper motions of the stars themselves, and so on. The second need is to observe and study the motions of the Moon and the planets past the stars. Ultimately it appears from this study that the spinning Earth is not the best clock we can have, and better time-keepers have to be discovered. And everything in astronomy works in two ways at once – astronomers need accurate time for their observations and they have to determine accurate time from their observations, they need 'fixed' stars in order to make accurate observations, but the accurate observation of the non-fixity of the stars gives vital information about the behaviour and evolution of the stellar system; and so it always goes on. Again, obviously, one thing leads to another – the motions of the stars that are of first concern are those across the line of sight, but those along the line of sight can be measured by spectroscopic means and this requires an expansion of astronomy into new types of observation. But this then makes the astronomer interested in the stars for their own sakes, and so opens up the whole of astrophysics, and thence leads on to the study of the entire universe of galaxies.

Such development is possible only along with one in instruments and their use, from the simple optics but finest dividing of circles of King Charles's time to the sophisticated optics and fantastically intricate electronics of our own time, from the careful study of human errors of observation to the elimination of the human element in much observational work, from Airy's marshalling of small armies of human computers to one central electronic computer serving all departments simultaneously, and from Pond's dropping of a time ball to the Rugby time-signal controlled by atomic frequency standards that are constant to one part in a million million.

Developments of both sorts involve other sciences. Astronomers interested in navigation were bound to be interested in geomagnetism, and the study of the geomagnetic field soon leads to that of solar-terrestrial relations and on to solar physics. In King Charles's time astronomy was almost the whole of exact science and its development then led to much of the rest of science. In our time, the movement has tended to be the other way, the development of other sciences bringing new techniques to astronomy. But in the latest times, astronomers are looking for new physics in the behaviour of neutron stars, black holes and other objects that are being discovered by these new techniques.

These general considerations are easily expressed in terms of the history of the Royal Observatory and its astronomers. Flamsteed and Pond produced famous catalogues of stars. Halley made a heroic study of the motion of the Moon. Bradley discovered aberration and nutation. Maskelyne produced a revolution in the practice of navigation. Airy reduced the planetary and lunar observations of his predecessors so that they made possible the discovery of a new planet, and he harnessed the technology of the industrial revolution to the service of exact science. Christie led the way into modern physical astronomy. Dyson more than anyone made photographic methods serve the most precise ends of astronomy, and so he and his colleagues were the first to test a crucial prediction of Einstein's general relativity. Spencer Jones established that the Earth is not rotating uniformly and went on to develop new methods of time-keeping. Woolley led the way in applying modern resources of observation and computing to study the dynamics and evolution of our own Galaxy. Burbidge promoted interest in the activity of galaxies in general. Woolley and Hunter have fostered the use of the latest techniques in optical astronomy and the collaboration with astronomers working in other parts of the electromagnetic spectrum and in cosmic radiation; also they have been prominent in extending the activity of British astronomers to observatories beyond our shores in both northern and southern hemispheres. Throughout the whole history there has been steadily increasing international cooperation.

The story of all this development is outlined in the following pages. They can give only a sketch of three centuries of endeavour by some of the most talented individuals of their times. The Observatory has been a pioneer in most things that it has done. As such, it has inevitably made mistakes and come in for criticism. Yet the fact is there for all to see that it has gone from strength to strength and has for a century past, at least, attracted many of this country's leading astronomers either to devote their scientific lives to its service, or to work there before moving on to positions of distinction throughout the world. Two other points are quite evident. One is the merit of having in at least one place in the world one observatory where all the main branches of optical astronomy are pursued alongside each other; we have only to look at the annual report to see how fruitful is their interaction – often in most unlikely ways. The other is that effectively all the work could be done only in a nationally supported establishment, with the assurance of being able to prosecute fundamental programs over long periods with no prospect of easy prizes; also much of the work is increasingly in the way of service to astronomers in other centres.

The Royal Observatory is part of the country's and the world's scientific heritage. The Greenwich meridian and Greenwich time are known everywhere, its work in fundamental positional astronomy is simply taken for granted, its work in the most modern optical astronomy with the most modern instrumental aids is known to all astronomers. Besides all this, it is well to remember that it gave birth to the *Nautical Almanac* and it once again provides the home for HM Nautical Almanac Office, as well as being the foster parent of the Institute of Navigation; seeing that the founding father of the Royal Meteorological Society did nearly all his work at the Observatory, it stands in very close relationship to British meteorology; for obvious reasons it is closely allied to British horology; because of its more than century-long record of observation and discovery in geomagnetism, it may claim a parental relationship to the science of geophysics which explains the happy kinship of British geophysics and British astronomy.

Our Astronomical Observator 1675–1719

The middle part of the seventeenth century was a time of scientific awakening in Western Europe that culminated in the heroic age of British science with the founding of the Royal Society in 1660 and with the work of Robert Boyle (1627–1691), Robert Hooke (1635–1703), Isaac Newton (1642–1727), Edmond Halley (1656–1742), and many others. The most highly developed part of physical science being astronomy, it was natural for the spirit of the times to express itself in the setting up of the first 'modern' observatories in Copenhagen, 1637 and 1650, Danzig 1641, Paris (built 1667–71), Lund 1670, and the Royal Observatory, Greenwich 1675. Nevertheless the immediate aim of the Paris Observatory was the improvement of geodesy, and that of the Royal Observatory was the improvement of navigation, rather than the advancement of pure astronomy.

The chief difficulty in knowing position at sea is for the mariner to determine his longitude with the aid of instruments usable on shipboard. Longitude measured from a standard meridian is equivalent to the difference between (easily determined) local time and time on that meridian by some standard clock. In the year 1674 a young Frenchman calling himself Sieur de St Pierre, being apparently under the protection of Louise de Kéroualle (later Duchess of Portsmouth), suggested to KING CHARLES II (1630–85) that the Moon moving across the background of the stars could serve as the required clock. His suggestion was not original, but his choice of its recipient was. The King promptly appointed a few men of learning to report upon it; these included SIR JONAS MOORE (1617–79), Surveyor-General of the Ordnance, and he in turn enlisted the service of one JOHN FLAMSTEED (1646–1719). Moore had known him for some years as a largely self-taught but highly accomplished young astronomer, and had tried to get the Royal Society to build him an observatory. Flamsteed at once pointed out that neither the motion of the Moon nor the positions of the stars were known with the required accuracy. When the King heard this he declared 'he must have them anew observed, examined and corrected, for the use of his seamen' and that Flamsteed was the man to do this. His Majesty proceeded to appoint him 'our astronomical observator, forthwith to apply himself with the most exact care and diligence to the rectifying the tables of the motions of the heavens, and the places of the fixed stars, so as to find out the so-much-desired longitude of places for the perfecting of the art of navigation'. On 4 March 1675 he issued to the office of the Ordnance the Warrant for the payment from St Michael's day, 1674, of Flamsteed's salary of one hundred pounds a year. At the age of 28, Flamsteed thus became the first Astronomer Royal, although any official sanction for this title came only much later; Flamsteed never used it, but did frequently sign after his name 'MR' or 'Mathematicus Regius'.

A second Warrant dated 22 June 1675 directed the Master-General of the Ordnance to build 'a small observatory within our park at Greenwich' to the design of SIR CHRISTOPHER WREN, 'provided that the whole sum, so to be expended or paid, shall not exceed five hundred pounds'. Wren (1632–1723) had been a professional astronomer and it was he who recommended the Greenwich site; it may well have been the best in England then and for the next 250 years. Flamsteed himself laid the foundation stone on 10 August 1675, and he moved in during the following July. 'Flamsteed House', the name long given to Wren's building for the Observator's habitation, now forms part of the National Maritime Museum and contains many of the Observatory's historic instruments.

Charles II seems not to have taken further interest. The Board of Ordnance gave Flamsteed £26 a year for a workman but nothing to pay for skilled assistance or to buy instruments. In order to get the necessary funds, he took many pupils in mathematics and astronomy, including boys from the 'Royal Mathematical School within Christ's Hospital'; he was notably successful in this, but he grudged the time it took from his Observatory work. One result was that he regarded his astronomical results as his private property, to be published only when and how he chose.

Flamsteed was the first astronomer systematically to use telescopic sights on all his instruments. His first main instrument was a sextant of nearly 7 feet radius mounted almost as an equatorial telescope. Chiefly with this, in the next 13 years he made single-handed some 20,000 observations. These resulted in a very substantially improved knowledge of the relative positions of the stars, but they were published only in 1712, and then only under pressure from the Royal Society. When his private finances improved in 1688, he engaged the instrument-maker ABRAHAM SHARP (1653–1742) to construct a mural arc also of nearly 7 feet radius with which, starting in 1689, he observed absolute positions of stars and planets with greater accuracy than had ever been achieved by anyone else. ('Absolute' here means relative to a well-defined over-all reference system on the celestial sphere, not relative merely to other particular objects in the sky.) Sharp assisted with the observations and calculations and he remained a devoted friend to Flamsteed even after returning to his native Yorkshire about 1700.

Flamsteed's aim was to produce a great *British Catalogue* of stars; a considerable part was printed by the time of his death at the end of 1719, but it took his last assistant JOSEPH CROSTHWAIT, aided by Sharp, another 6 years to complete its publication for Flamsteed's widow in *Historia coelestis britannica* 1725. It then served to establish Flamsteed as the greatest systematic astronomer since the invention of the telescope; the methods he developed had a lasting influence. Amongst other contributions, he discovered the mutual influence of Jupiter and Saturn on their motions, and he determined the characteristics of the axial rotation of the Sun. Flamsteed also had pioneering ideas about a zenith telescope and actually used a 90-foot well dug in the observatory ground in order to mount an instrument of very long focal length. His ambition in doing this was to measure stellar parallax, the apparent displacement of a star due to the movement of the Earth in its orbit around the Sun, but he seems to have had to abandon it after only a few trials. Parallax was not in fact detected until more than a century after Flamsteed's death; the idea of observing close to the zenith, however, was exploited with great success by several of his successors. At a more practical level, starting in 1683 Flamsteed published tables of high water at London Bridge with rules for deriving results for other ports. In his lifetime, his undoubtedly high reputation largely depended, however, upon his extensive correspondence with leading astronomers at home and abroad, rather than upon his published work.

Flamsteed was an excessively serious conscientious man, who was in chronically poor health, and who spent a lifetime of overwork in a single job with very little assistance and not much encouragement from scientific colleagues. It is small wonder that he became tetchy and quick to note largely imagined defects in others. Also, while pre-eminent in his profession, he scarcely appreciated the greater movements of thought of the age in which he lived. So Flamsteed's relations with his famous contemporaries, particularly Newton, Halley and Hooke, deteriorated into a miserable state. Much of the trouble arose from his reluctance to publish his results by instalments, and parts of this story are frequently recounted. One good outcome of the unhappy situation was QUEEN ANNE's Warrant of 1710 appointing the President of the Royal Society along with other Fellows to serve as Visitors, which ensured that the affairs of the Royal Observatory should not again fall into such a state of isolation from the general life of the scientific community.

The Halley Succession
1720-1835

E. Halley

Flamsteed left the Observatory without staff or instruments. The instruments he had were his own and they went to his widow. It was indeed fortunate for the whole future of British astronomy that there was available a scientist of the highest repute, who had abundant experience of organizing scientific investigations and affairs generally, who was on close and cordial terms with other leading scientists and public men, and who had for many years been intimately associated with the Royal Society – even though he was a man of 63 and one with whom Flamsteed had latterly quarrelled most bitterly. On the recommendation of the Lord Chancellor, the Earl of Macclesfield, on 9 February 1720 King George I appointed EDMOND HALLEY 'Our Astronomical Observator in Our Observatory at Greenwich'. Halley was then Savilian Professor of Geometry at Oxford and he retained that post and its emoluments for the rest of his life. He was one of the greatest scientists ever, and undoubtedly the most gifted scientist of all the Astronomers Royal. Coming to the position at the age he did, his most original work even in astronomy had already been accomplished, so that it does not form part of the record of the Observatory. However, Halley was still full of vigour and he made a substantial contribution to its story.

By 1714 the problem of determining longitude at sea had become so clamant that Parliament had passed an Act offering rewards up to £20,000 for a successful method, and appointing the Board of Longitude to adjudicate in the matter. As Astronomer Royal, Halley was commissioned to concern himself with this problem, and he was interested also in the possibility of winning a reward; so he returned to the method of lunar distances. He saw that greatly improved tables of the Moon's motion would be needed, and he planned to observe the motion throughout an entire rotation of the Moon's nodes, the 18.6-year period after which the motion of the Moon over the background of the stars is closely repeated – quite an ambition for a man aged 63. For this, he had to re-equip the observatory. He installed a transit telescope for finding the time when a celestial object crosses the meridian, which yields the astronomical longitude of the object or, conversely, checks the time if the longitude ('right ascension') is known. This was the first in the series of famous instruments of this sort that have established and maintained the great reputation of Greenwich for 'fundamental' astronomy through the centuries of its existence. Halley ordered besides an

8-foot mural quadrant (delivered 1724) by the use of which the astronomical latitude, or 'declination', of an object was to be determined; this was a replacement for Flamsteed's 7-foot quadrant. For these instruments Halley secured a grant of £500 from the Board of Ordnance. This was spent by 1726, when the Visitors reported to the Royal Society that it had 'been laid out with as much frugality and good husbandry as was consistent with the putting the Instruments in such a state of perfection as the business of his Majesty's Royal Observatory required'. But also 'there is wanting to finish and put the observatory in right order a further sum of £200'. Apparently Halley secured this as well. So began the long history in the scientific world of applications for grants and supplementary grants.

Between 1722 and 1740 Halley observed some 1,500 meridian transits of the Moon. It is claimed that he missed scarcely any opportunity to make such an observation. Only during the last two or three years did he have some assistance, notably from James Bradley (1693–1762), who was then Savilian Professor of Astronomy in Oxford. In 1726 Newton, as President of the Royal Society, took Halley to task for not publishing his observations; but Halley pleaded that 'great rewards having been appointed by act of Parliament' he wanted to complete his work before others might take advantage of reaping the benefit of his labours. Halley's astronomical tables edited by JOHN BEVIS (1693–1771) appeared posthumously in 1749, although he had had them printed 20 years earlier. However, the bulk of his observations were taken away by his family after his death and only in 1765 found their way back to the Observatory, where they repose bound into four neat volumes. But they have never been published. In fact Halley's observations scarcely attained the accuracy demanded for their purpose; he took no account of fractional parts of seconds of time, and he considered 10 seconds of arc as the 'utmost attainable limit of accuracy'. However, his work did prepare the way for the more refined measurements made by his successors. Amongst other work done as Astronomer Royal, Halley published in 1721 the first 'accurate table of refraction' by the Earth's atmosphere.

The first Royal Visit to the Observatory took place in 1729, when George II's consort, QUEEN CAROLINE, was very favourably impressed, and this had useful practical consequences, notably a Post Captain's half pay for Halley to supplement his slender income as Astronomer Royal.

J. Bradley

Flamsteed observed the star Gamma Draconis close to the zenith and he detected an apparent displacement of the star depending upon the time of year. He believed he had detected parallax, i.e. the apparent displacement of a star depending upon the *position* of the Earth in its orbit around the Sun. Robert Hooke had claimed a similar result. In 1729 JAMES BRADLEY rediscovered this 'aberration' effect for a number of stars and succeeded in explaining it as depending upon the *velocity* of the Earth in its orbit as related to the velocity of light coming from the star – a very great intellectual achievement. This remains one of the most celebrated discoveries in astronomy, but its story is not part of the record of the Royal Observatory. It was one of the reasons for which Halley, who had known Bradley since he was a young man, had such a high opinion of him. Indeed, about 1736, Halley wanted to resign in favour of Bradley, but his resignation had not been accepted. However, when Halley died in 1742, Bradley was clearly marked out as his successor; KING GEORGE II appointed him forthwith.

Bradley was one of the greatest observational astronomers ever. He acquired improved instruments, some of which remained in use for up to one hundred years; he pioneered modern methods of using them, determining their errors, allowing for the effect of temperature and barometric pressure; he produced by far the best tables of refraction of his time and for long afterwards; he made observations and discoveries of permanent importance, and he prepared the way for important work by his successors.

Upon his appointment, Bradley got busy with the instruments he found at Greenwich, but he also started planning a 'new observatory' there. In 1748 the Royal Society on Bradley's behalf presented to the Lords Commissioners of the Admiralty a petition for £1,000 for the proposed new instruments and buildings. Its success was one of the most important landmarks in the history of the Royal Observatory. It is interesting also as the first recorded direct contact with the Admiralty instead of with the Board of Ordnance itself, then subordinate to the Admiralty and Treasury.

The new instruments were mainly for observations in the meridian and Bradley's new building was specially designed to receive them, partly by incorporating Halley's meridian wall. He also caused to be re-erected his own zenith telescope, with which he had done his main work on aberration, and with which he proceeded to complete his work on his other great discovery of nutation – the nodding of the Earth's axis produced by the gravitation of the Moon – published in 1748, for which he was that year awarded the Copley Medal of the Royal Society. Also he obtained an equatorial sector intended for measuring the angular distance to a comet from nearby fixed stars; it was mounted on a polar axis and was the first instrument of its kind. In this connexion it is interesting to note that Bradley, as a young man working with his uncle James Pound (1669–1724), had used the first, or almost the first, clock-driven equatorial telescope. Nearly all these instruments were made by, or under the supervision of, GEORGE GRAHAM (1675–1751) or by JOHN BIRD (1709-76). Little is said here about instruments and their makers; happily they will have a book to themselves (see bibliography). The Royal Observatory has been indeed fortunate in almost all its instrument makers; they have appreciated the degree of precision that has been required of them, and many, like these two, have attained a fame of their own by making possible the observations upon which so much of man's knowledge of the universe depends. In particular, Bird received a well-merited award of £500 from the Board of Longitude.

Bradley determined the positions of some 3,000 stars with a precision never before attained, the uncertainty being only about 1 arc-second. This work formed the basis for all subsequent work on the proper motions of the stars, which is still one of the parts of fundamental astronomy in which the Royal Greenwich Observatory is pre-eminent, and from which a great part of what is known about the structure of the Galaxy is ultimately derived. Bradley also did important work upon the motion of Jupiter's satellites, which he was then able to use as a standard clock in his precise determination of the longitudes of Lisbon and New York. He was perpetually concerned too with determining the distance of the Sun; his last work was in preparation for the observation to this end of the transit of Venus in 1761. In consequence, it was successfully observed at Greenwich and at St Helena. Unfortunately Bradley became painfully ill about this time; he died the following year. His assistant from 1756 to 1760 had been CHARLES MASON (1730–87) – of the 'Mason-Dixon Line' in the USA, also the one who made the survey that led to the choice of Schiehallion for Maskelyne's famous experiment on gravitation – and by instruction of the Royal Society he observed the transit of Venus of 1761 from the Cape of Good Hope and that of 1769 from Ireland. As things turned out, it was many years before the 1761 and 1769 observations were used in order to calculate a value of the solar parallax – by J. F. Encke about 1820 – the result being the best to date but, as we now know, nearly 3 percent too small.

N. Bliss

NATHANIEL BLISS (1700–64) had succeeded Halley as Savilian Professor of Geometry and he had given Bradley a certain amount of assistance at Greenwich. Also Bradley had enlisted him to substitute for himself in observing the transit of Venus in 1761 at Greenwich. So once again the succession was well indicated and Bliss became the new Astronomer Royal in 1762. However, he died only two years later without having had the chance to leave his mark upon the Royal Observatory.

N. Maskelyne

The next incumbent virtually selected himself – without intending it, because he could not have expected the vacancy to occur. NEVIL MASKELYNE (1732–1811) had a different background from that of the first four Astronomers Royal; he was a man of substance, he was set upon a career in the

Church, he never held any academic appointment, and in astronomy he was in 1764 still an amateur. In 1755 he was ordained to the curacy of Barnet and about then he came to know Bradley and to assist him in his work; they became close friends. Bradley got the Royal Society to send Maskelyne to observe the transit of Venus of 1761 from St Helena (since a transit enables the distance of the Sun to be determined only if it is observed from stations in at least two different latitudes) and he did this successfully. However, the voyage itself inspired in Maskelyne his chief scientific interest, the old problem of finding longitude at sea, particularly by the method of lunar distances. He tested the method himself, and he arranged for it to be tested by the masters of four East Indiamen. Being thereby convinced of its practical feasibility, he published in 1763 the *British Mariner's Guide* on the subject. This was the forerunner of all nautical almanacs published anywhere in the world.

As we know, the Royal Observatory existed for the express purpose of supplying the astronomical observations upon which such operations could be based, and successive Astronomers Royal had dutifully made these observations. At a meeting of the Royal Society on 9 June 1763, Maskelyne made a forceful – though perhaps florid – statement about the ill consequences of the Astronomers Royal having, however, regarded the observations made at Greenwich as their own exclusive property. The Society resolved to enquire into the rights of the matter, to use the best means of securing past and future observations for general availability, to publish past observations when obtained, and to require the Astronomer Royal in future to deliver his observations annually for publication in *Philosophical Transactions*.

In the course of the ensuing activity, the Society discovered that it had forgotten the most famous thing about Queen Anne – the fact that she was dead. Her Warrant to the Visitors had no effect after her death, and so for forty years it had been acting without authority. Anyhow, KING GEORGE III put things right with a new Warrant of 22 February 1765 and thence forward every Sovereign issued one soon after coming to the throne. The King then approved 'Regulations for the due execution of the office of Astronomer Royal' put forward by the thus legitimized Visitors. Meanwhile he had in February 1765 appointed Maskelyne, who was thus required to carry out these Regulations which in fact he had himself drafted before Bliss's unexpected death. He did this conscientiously for the next 46 years and, in particular, he regularly published all his observations, first with the Royal Society and then from 1776 as separately published *Greenwich Observations*, sponsored by the Visitors. Some 500 copies were printed each time; about 50 of these were presented to various observatories, etc., and the remainder became the property of the Astronomer Royal, so that some vestige of the earlier claims to proprietorship was actually officially recognized.

In 1768 Bliss's executor conveyed to the Royal Observatory the observations made during his short tenure. In 1765 Halley's daughter gave the Royal Society the collection of his notes and observations which it put in the charge of the Astronomer Royal, being those already mentioned. Some years later the Board of Longitude bought Flamsteed's papers from his heirs and deposited them in the Observatory. Bradley's observations had been carried off by his executors – in a fashion that was out of character for the man himself – and were not published, on their behalf, until Volume I appeared in 1798 and Volume II in 1805; and in 1861 Oxford University eventually returned the manuscript to Greenwich. Then at last the Observatory possessed the unbroken series of observations since its foundation nearly 200 years before.

All this naturally makes us wonder how the Observatory managed to acquire its reputation for pre-eminence when, for so long, so much of its basic work remained inaccessible. Part of the answer seems to be that it was known to possess in general better and more novel equipment than was to be found elsewhere. Also the modern idea that a scientist should publish his work as soon as possible took a long time to develop – and, of course, it may change again as new means of storage and retrieval are developed – the private exchange of ideas and results being relatively more important in the early days. Above all, the directors had made or been concerned in developments, researches and discoveries in astronomy and science generally much excelling in the aggregate those made in other countries. This was well illustrated in the case of Maskelyne, to whom we now return.

Maskelyne's greatest contribution was in conceiving and, with the help of the Board of Longitude, in producing from 1766 onwards the *Nautical Almanac*. Each year, starting for 1767, it provided tables of all the astronomical information required by navigators and by practical astronomers. It met with immediate success and it has flourished ever since – apart from certain vicissitudes around 1820 – being now produced in various subdivisions by highly organized international collaboration. Originally Maskelyne had to rely considerably upon tables of the motion of the Moon and other bodies produced in Germany – by TOBIAS MAYER (1723–62) in Göttingen using a quadrant made by Bird and presented by George II – and in France, but as time went on the *Almanac* came to depend much more upon Greenwich observations and tables. Maskelyne was fortunate in his three assistants, whose work he organized very effectively. They produced also *Tables requisite to be used with the Ephemeris*, which simplified the use of the *Almanac;* it is recorded that the 1781 edition of these *Tables* sold 10,000 copies on publication.

The other much-desired navigational aid was a reliable sea-going chronometer. JOHN HARRISON (1693–1776) had made much progress in this regard, and in 1761 he had submitted his No. 4 in a final bid for the Board of Longitude prize. The Royal Observatory was much concerned in adjudicating. In the final test on a voyage to Barbados in 1764, the Observatory assistant CHARLES GREEN was officially in charge, but Maskelyne (having no idea that he was soon to become Astronomer Royal) had accompanied him in the capacity of chaplain to *HMS Princess Louisa* in which they both made the trip. Indeed, Maskelyne had been commissioned to test Mayer's tables by observing lunar distances on the voyage, for these tables had also been submitted for the prize originally through Bradley. Harrison No. 4 made the voyage in *HMS Tartar* and it achieved brilliant success. Consideration of the allocation of the prize dragged on for several years, with Maskelyne (by then Astronomer Royal) playing an important advisory rôle. Eventually Mayer's widow received £3,000 in 1765, and by 1773 Harrison had received the full amount of £20,000 originally offered in 1714, accepting the Board's figures for the various instalments.

Maskelyne is remembered for another romantic episode in British science, the weighing of the Earth. Astronomical methods give, often with high accuracy, the gravitational masses of celestial bodies including the Earth. In order to express these in terms of the standard pound (a copy of which happens to be in custody of the Royal Observatory), it is necessary to find a body for which both sorts of mass are measurable. A mountain may be such a body. If it is sufficiently well surveyed and if the rock composing it is known, then its mass can be estimated in pounds. If a plumb-line is suspended near the mountain, its deflexion from the vertical yields a measure of the ratio of the gravitational mass of the mountain to that of the Earth. In 1774, on this principle, Maskelyne used the mountain Schiehallion in Scotland. He had to measure angles of deflexion of less than one-hundredth of a degree, which he succeeded in doing by astronomical methods. He found for the mean density of the Earth $4\frac{1}{2}$ times that of water; it was the best value got up to that time, although the true value is about $5\frac{1}{2}$.

Maskelyne's published routine observations, made with help from never more than one assistant, number some 90,000. After his death, the observing books were reported to have been 'kept with the utmost regularity'.

J. Pond

JOHN POND (1767 – 1836) was a distinguished private astronomer who discovered from his own observations that Bird's mural quadrant, in use at Greenwich since 1750, was producing some unreliable results. In consequence, in 1806 Maskelyne presented to the Visitors a memorial about his instruments, and in due course they appointed a committee – latterly including Pond – which recommended a mural circle of 6-foot diameter to be made by E. TROUGHTON (1753 – 1835). It was not finished until after Maskelyne's death in office in 1811. He had recommended Pond as his successor, and at the Visitation that year Pond's appointment by the Prince Regent was read. On the same occasion the Visitors ordered a 'weeding' of the instruments, and this foreshadowed one of the main interests of Pond's directorship; he was to become known for raising the accuracy of observations to a level never before attained.

In 1811 C. Jenkinson (later Lord Liverpool) presented an equatorial telescope that had belonged to SIR GEORGE SHUCKBURGH. It was the first such telescope, and then only a modest 4.2 inch aperture though well-mounted, possessed by the Royal Observatory, and it was also the first of several notable major gifts from private persons that have enriched the resources of our national observatory. In 1812 the mural circle ordered by Maskelyne was installed; it was to give trouble a little later, but in 1822 Pond could report it to be 'even more perfect' than when it was first erected. The experience suggested to him, however, that he should have a second circle as well; this turned out to exceed 'in every respect the most sanguine expectations', and Pond worked out ways of increasing the accuracy of his observations by using the two circles in conjunction. Also it was Pond who introduced the mercury trough to give an artificial horizon for circle observations a technique widely followed ever since. Pond acquired, too, a reflecting telescope of 10-foot focal length made by the great William Herschel; he modernized and diversified the instrumentation of the Observatory in various other ways.

Mention of the name of Herschel calls for some explanation of the fact that two of the greatest astronomers produced by this country, WILLIAM HERSCHEL, (1738 – 1822) and JOHN HERSCHEL (1792 – 1871) feature so little in the public history of the national observatory. The reason is briefly that they were pioneers in the study of the physical constitution of the stellar universe; while they had to make use of the sort of astronomy carried on at Greenwich most of their work did not immediately react upon the work at Greenwich. Personally, however, they were on friendly terms with the Greenwich astronomers, and both Herschels served regularly as Visitors.

Pond's directorship pursued a less even course than that of any other Astronomer Royal, but his distractions were mostly in the nature of growing pains of the Royal Observatory and of science as a whole. In 1816 the Visitors, presumably at Pond's instance, pointed to the inconvenience experienced by the Astronomer Royal because he had to deal with three of the public offices of Government – Treasury, Admiralty, Board of Ordnance. They suggested the Lords Commissioners of the Admiralty as 'the most proper in every respect to take . . . the whole charge and management . . .'. For the first time, also, mention was made of a special relationship with the Hydrographer of the Admiralty, (later 'of the Navy'), who in the person

PLATE 1

Greenwich

Flamsteed's Sextant 1676

Pond's 10-foot Transit Instrument 1816

Halley's 8-foot Quadrant 1725

Airy's Transit Circle 1851

PLATE 2

Greenwich

Flamsteed House 1675-6

Meridian Building

'Physical Observatory' 1891-9

PLATE 3

Herstmonceux

Castle and Isaac Newton Telescope Dome

Equatorial Group of Telescopes

Castle and grounds

Royal Arms of the Founder

Herstmonceux Castle

PLATE 4

Herstmonceux

Isaac Newton and Equatorial Telescopes

30-inch Reflector

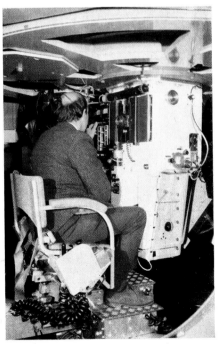

Isaac Newton Telescope: Cassegrain
spectrograph

Isaac Newton Telescope:
coudé spectrograph

of many distinguished holders of that office came thenceforth to play an important logistic part in the running of the Royal Observatory, although the Hydrographer was first made a Visitor only by the Warrant of 1858. The transfer occurred in 1818 apparently with no more formal notification than a chit from the Board of Ordnance to say that bills for payment had been transmitted to the Lords Commissioners.

One consequence was that in 1821 the Royal Observatory took charge of the chronometers of the Royal Navy, a considerable addition to its work for which no immediate increase in its staff was provided. Indeed, the matter of assistants to cope with the steadily increasing activity of the Royal Observatory was a perpetual preoccupation for Pond and, when he did get a modest increase in numbers, the question of adequate renumeration was a further one. Actually one scheme put forward by Pond in 1823 did elicit a surprisingly ready response from the Admiralty, which was prepared to regard the appointment of some well-qualified assistants as an opportunity to encourage astronomical and mathematical studies. For in those times of the start of the industrial revolution these lacked the sort of encouragement given to more practical sciences. The Royal Society responded cordially to what they repeatedly termed these 'enlightened views'; but even this turned sour on Pond. He had no success in recruiting highly qualified candidates, and in any case for much of the work he required merely 'drudges of a superior order'. Pond used the phrase in a personal letter which unfortunately found its way to the Admiralty. It clearly considered that its enlightened initiative had been frustrated and, when Pond applied for better terms for his lower grade assistants, it was in no mood to help him.

Pond had inherited the responsibility for producing the *Nautical Almanac* but apparently not his predecessor's staff for this work. He was also much more taken up with instrumental developments than Maskelyne had been. In consequence, the *Almanac* fell into disrepute. As the result of an Act of 1818, the *Almanac* was then removed from the responsibilities of the Observatory, and the scientist THOMAS YOUNG (1773 – 1829) was appointed Superintendent. He effected some improvement, but more reform was needed. Young died in 1829, and no less a person than G. B. AIRY applied to succeed him. However, the Admiralty decided that it devolved upon the Astronomer Royal. So Pond had to tackle the task afresh; he did, in fact, produce some further reforms, and he invited some assistance from Airy in doing so. Nevertheless the Admiralty took further advice which led to a separate Nautical Almanac Office being again set up to produce the *Almanac* for 1834 and onwards, and thus the subject goes outside this history for a century. In the course of all these happenings, the Board of Longitude was abolished by 'An Act repealing the Laws now in force relating to the Discovery of the Longitude at Sea' of 15 July 1828; the records of its long service to the nation are preserved in the care of the Royal Observatory at Herstmonceux.

One particular service had been rendered in 1820 when the Board, including Pond and also Sir Joseph Banks (1743 – 1820), President of the Royal Society 1778 – 1820, as Commissioners, proposed the establishment of an Observatory at the Cape of Good Hope. This was placed in the charge of the Admiralty, but it was not formally linked with the Royal Observatory until much later. However, Pond was naturally consulted about staff and instruments in the early days.

Another event of significance for British astronomy took place in 1820 — the foundation of the Astronomical Society, that became 'Royal' in 1830. Although Pond was not active in forming or running the young Society he accepted office as one of the Vice-Presidents elected at its first meeting. When the formidable Banks put obstacles in its way it was reported that Pond 'made a very spirited reply'. The Admiralty consulted the Society in 1830 about the reform of the *Nautical Almanac*, and Pond (along with Airy) was a member of the sub-committee of ten that formulated the resulting famous Report.

The advent of the Astronomical Society also affected the Observatory nearer home. For the Warrant of 9 September 1830, issued by William IV after his accession in June, set up an entirely re-constituted Board of Visitors composed of the President and five Fellows of the Royal Society, the President and five Fellows of the Astronomical Society, the Savilian Professor of Astronomy at Oxford and the Plumian Professor of Astronomy at Cambridge; the President of the Royal Society was to be Chairman or, in his absence, the President of the Astronomical Society. The following January the Admiralty asked the recently elected President of the Royal Society, HRH the Duke of Sussex (1773 – 1843) to call a meeting of the Board at the Admiralty to consider measures for the more effective and rapid publications of the Greenwich and Cape Observations. In the event, the board held no fewer than eight meetings in 1831, including the mandatory Visitation in June. The Plumian Professor was Airy, who thus began his intimate association with the Observatory which meant that he attended nearly every meeting of the Visitors for the next 60 years; he had indeed been an invited Visitor under the older régime in each of the years 1827–30. At the first meeting he noted that Pond 'was in a rather feeble state', and later he wrote, 'I cannot represent too strongly how completely Mr Pond's spirit has been broken down by the interference of the Visitors'.

For several years Pond had been plagued by a first assistant and his family who used him disgracefully and brought the Observatory into ill repute. As a result, Pond 'suffered grievous depression of body and mind' which drove him to take four months' leave in the later part of 1831, but he continued in office for another four years. Towards the end of this time he drafted General Regulations for the conduct of the Observatory by his successor, most of which Airy subsequently thoroughly approved.

Pond resigned in 1835 and died in 1836; he was buried in Halley's tomb in Lee churchyard. Maskelyne and he had both added much to the store of good observations; in addition, Maskelyne's experience of organizing the work of the *Nautical Almanac*, and Pond's experience of getting new instruments and then getting the best possible results from them were invaluable to the man who came after them.

There remains another memorial. Every day at 1 o'clock the Greenwich time-ball drops on its mast above Wren's original building of the Royal Observatory. That first public time-signal in the land was installed in 1833 by John Pond.

Full Vigour 1835–1933

G. B. Airy

GEORGE BIDDELL AIRY (1801 – 92) was the greatest Astronomer Royal as such and one of the most remarkable men that this country has produced. By the age of 27 he had won all the highest distinctions that Cambridge had to offer to a mathematician, he had held the Lucasian Professorship once held by Newton, he had transferred to the Plumian Professorship and he was installed as Director of the University's quite new Observatory. By the end of 1835 he had a Civil List pension (settled upon his wife), he had declined a Knighthood, and he was established as seventh Astronomer Royal.

Throughout his long life, Airy was a prodigious worker. The list of his published papers contains over 500 items besides which he wrote over 140 official reports and the like and about a dozen books. He wrote thousands of letters, all in his own hand, never having a secretary or clerk to help him; and he kept all his mountainous records in perfect order. All this was possible only because he was methodical beyond belief.

The array of Airy's qualifications for the directorship was formidable. He was the best professional astronomer of the time and he was at the best age to tackle the problems and responsibilities that confronted him; he had had the best available experience; having been a Visitor for several years he well knew the Observatory's state, and the possibility of his becoming its director had been discussed with him on behalf of the government over more than a year; his position in Cambridge gave him unique advantage in finding staff to go with him; as President of the Royal Astronomical Society, as a recent member of the Board of Longitude, and in many other ways, he was well acquainted with his fellow scientists; he had made himself familiar with observatories in Europe. He brought to his task a remarkable flair for administration; for instance, if he needed a new instrument, he stated in the plainest terms what he wanted, why he wanted it, where he would site it, who would make it, how much it would cost to buy and to operate, and he would exhibit drawings or a model. He never disparaged the instruments that were being superseded. Although the scope of the Observatory increased greatly under his direction, he never asked for more than that for which he had actual need; he always used his manpower in the most efficient and economical manner possible. So he always got what he proposed and, when he had it, it always turned out to be even somewhat better than he had predicted. He was, indeed, an outstanding exponent of the 'art of the possible'. And he exemplified all the strengths of Victorian England: he had unquestioning confidence in the abilities of engineers, instrument-makers, opticians, and so on, of the time to produce instruments with all the rigidity and precision, and all the accessories, that he proposed.

Airy organized the work of the establishment with extraordinary effectiveness; he regularly acknowledged the good work of his staff and of instrument-makers and others who worked for him. During all his long term of office he seemed to become ever more effective. He had a robust appreciation of the importance of his office – 'I am not a mere Superintendent of current observations, but a Trustee for the honour of Greenwich Observatory generally, and for its general utility in the world'. So those who worked with him were invigorated by the conviction of working for the finest institution of its sort that had to have nothing but the best they had to offer. No man ever left a more permanent mark upon any scientific establishment, and the Airy tradition still pervades and inspires the RGO of to-day – even if the fashion of the time discourages somewhat the explicit mention of such influences. But at the same time Airy respected, and refused to encroach upon, the legitimate fields of 'local and private observatories'.

With such a catalogue of merits, where were the flaws? Perhaps the worst was that he had none – a few human failings might have earned him rather more warmth in the respect in which he was undoubtedly held. His rule was certainly despotic, but it has been suggested that some of Airy's reputation in this regard may have been partly earned for him by one or two of his overzealous lieutenants. Also, since Airy's early advancement had been so rapid it meant that his close associates at the time were appreciably older than himself; as years went on, therefore, he tended to be left without real friends, and this must have affected his behaviour.

Even in writing about Airy one feels the urge to be systematic and so we may briefly review some of the activities of his time under several headings:

Astronomical instruments   Airy gradually replaced all the instruments by new ones of his own design. Accepting that the first duty laid upon the Observatory was the precise determination of the motion of the Moon, he procured in 1847 his *altazimuth telescope* for accurate observations unrestricted to the meridian. This enormously increased the exactness of tables of the Moon's motion. Accepting that the second duty was the accurate determination of the positions of other heavenly bodies and thereby the precise measurement of time as determined by the rotation of the Earth, he procured his *transit circle*. It combined the offices of a transit instrument and a meridian circle. This most famous astronomical apparatus determined Greenwich time from 1851 until it was phased out of that particular duty in the 1930s, but (with only a little intermission) it continued in regular use until 1954 by which time it had served to observe about 700,000 transits. The major contemporary observatories acquired copies of Airy's transit circle. He took the object glass of the old transit telescope for his new *reflex zenith telescope* of 1851, the progenitor of a line of instruments culminating in the present *photographic zenith tube*, which is the most accurate astronomical instrument ever made.

At this stage Airy told the Visitors, 'I regard our equipment as approaching to a normal and quiet state more completely than it has been for several years past'. In spite of this and of the fact that he emphatically considered fundamental positional astronomy to be the overriding obligation of the Observatory, by 1855 he was addressing the Visitors on a proposition for a 'large' equatorial refracting telescope. For in this category, the Observatory still had no more than the Shuckburgh telescope presented in 1811 and one with a $6\frac{3}{4}$-inch object glass presented by R. Sheepshanks in 1837, and these seem never to have been put to much use. By 1860 Airy had his new telescope with a $12\frac{3}{4}$-inch object glass made by MERZ in Munich, and he proposed using it to make systematic scrutiny, with careful drawings, of the disks of the planets. In the course of the next 20 years, Airy and his colleagues used the telescope in pioneering work on stellar spectra and stellar radial velocities, on cometary spectra, and on stellar photography. After a long and useful career at Greenwich, this telescope still serves as the guider attached to the 26-inch refractor at Herstmonceux.

Magnetic, solar and meteorological observations Terrestrial magnetism had in one way or another been an interest of almost all the Astronomers Royal before Airy, and this may be regarded as the beginning of geophysics. Then from 1831 onwards the Visitors heard proposals for initiating regular observations of the Earth's magnetic field at Greenwich. There was at the time widespread interest in fluctuations in the field and their physical causes, and the great mathematician C. F. Gauss (1777 – 1855) in Göttingen had organized a 'Magnetic Union' of more than a dozen magnetic observatories in almost as many countries in western Europe. Airy had become interested and had discussed the subject with several scientists including Gauss; soon after he became Astronomer Royal he began to take action, ordering magnets, choosing a site and erecting a suitable non-magnetic building. Then in 1836 the Royal Society asked Airy and S. Hunter Christie to report upon a letter from Alexander von Humboldt to the President (the Duke of Sussex) proposing united efforts of all scientific societies in Europe in setting up magnetic observatories throughout the world. The report was strongly in favour of the proposal and gave a reasoned case which is of prophetic interest in mentioning explicitly that much might be learned about the Earth's upper atmosphere. All this magnetic work is significant too as the first deliberate international co-operation in science (apart from particular occasions like transits of Venus), and this always appealed to Airy. A still further interest is that it brings out a side of Airy's scientific activity that might not be evident from his work in fundamental astronomy and celestial mechanics. This was his simultaneous concern for more physical topics. He was a pioneer in giving lectures on magnetism in Cambridge, and all his life he was enthusiastic about applications of 'galvanism'.

The first magnetic observations of Airy's time were made at Greenwich in 1838. In 1841 J. Glaisher observed a great magnetic storm, and this served to emphasize the need for regular continuous recording. In 1847 Airy achieved this for the first time in any observatory by use of a photographic method due to Charles Brooke. Over the years the equipment has naturally been re-designed several times, but the essential features of Airy's system are still in use.

By a curious paradox for an astronomical observatory, the regular observation of the Sun at Greenwich was started, not directly because of its intrinsic interest as a heavenly body, but because of the association of fluctuations of the Earth's magnetic field with sunspots and other activity on the Sun. In 1873 Airy acquired the Kew photo-heliograph and installed it in a new dome; this instrument and its successors have been used ever since to make one or two direct photographs of the Sun's surface on every day when it has been visible, gaps in the record being remedied as necessary by observations overseas. In particular, this has produced a record of the size, position and movement of every sunspot that has appeared on the visible disk of the Sun during more than a century.

In 1873 Airy appointed E. W. MAUNDER (1851 – 1928) as Assistant for Photographic and Spectroscopic Observations. In 1904 Maunder first published his famous 'butterfly' diagram as a presentation of sunspot activity that vividly displays its cycle of eleven years. In such ways Airy initiated the work that gave Greenwich a leading place in the study of solar-terrestrial relations for many years to come. However, it appears that all ventures into more physical studies of the Sun and stars from 1870 onwards were instigated by Christie—who joined as Chief Assistant that year—encouraged by the distinguished amateur astronomers William Huggins (1824 – 1910) and Warren de la Rue (1815 – 89).

Early in his time at Greenwich, Airy was induced to start a full program of meteorological observations. He was always somewhat resentful about this, for not even Airy could impose law and order upon the Greenwich weather. Anyhow the unbroken record from 1840 to 1952 is one of the most valuable in existence. As a matter of organizational convenience the magnetic and meteorological work was always operated under the same member of the observatory staff, and since successive holders of the office happened to be notable personalities in their own right, it came to enjoy a measure of autonomy within the system.

Lunar and planetary observations J. B. J. Delambre (1749 – 1822) wrote in his great history of astronomy in the 18th century, 'One can truly say that, if in some great revolution the sciences came to be lost, and were this collection alone preserved . . one would find in it the wherewithal to reconstruct almost in its entirety the whole edifice of modern astronomy; such a claim may be made only for this unique collection, because besides the merit of a precision rarely achieved and never yet surpassed, it has also the additional merit of an unbroken sequence since 1750, which as a first epoch of observation leaves little to be desired'. The 'collection' was that of the Greenwich observations by Bradley and Maskelyne. Small wonder then that about the time of taking office, as heir to such riches, Airy embarked upon the task of reducing all the observations of planets made from 1750 to 1830 so that they gave as accurately as possible the motions of these bodies throughout that interval. He marshalled a group of several young men to work as computers eleven hours a day exclusively on this undertaking. The completed work appeared in 1845. Airy then tackled a similar task for the observations of the Moon, which he described as the greatest astronomical work ever undertaken; the finished work appeared in two volumes in 1848.

In 1841 a 22-year old Cambridge mathematician J. C. Adams (1819 – 92) 'formed a design . . . of investigating, as soon as possible after taking my degree, the irregularities of the motion of Uranus', his attention having been 'first directed to this subject . . . by reading Mr Airy's valuable Report on the recent progress of Astronomy' to the British Association 1831 – 33. He later recorded that Airy 'in the kindest possible manner, sent me in February 1844 the results of all the Greenwich observations of Uranus.' Adams sought to find whether the irregularities could be accounted for by the existence of another planet beyond Uranus. By September 1845 Adams had shown that this was so and had calculated the expected path in the sky of 'the new planet.' That autumn he made some attempt to enlist Airy's interest; Adams made no proposal for an observational search, and the evidence is that Airy supposed he was being consulted about publication. Only one short statement of results was all that Airy had had from Adams when in June 1846 he read a full published account of similar independent work by the French astronomer U. J. J. Le Verrier (1811 – 77) and he wrote a complimentary letter to Le Verrier about it. Unfortunately Airy omitted at that point to mention the work of Adams. The reply that Le Verrier sent to Airy was the first proposal for a search of the sky.

Within about a week, Airy asked his own successor in Cambridge to under-take this with a telescope that Airy had erected there and that he knew to be best suited to the purpose. As a result the planet was seen three times, but not recognized as such. Meanwhile Le Verrier had applied also to astronomers in Berlin, where on 23 September 1846 J. G. Galle discovered the planet, soon to become known as Neptune. The discovery was made because H. L. d'Arrest noted that an object observed by Galle, whom he was assisting, did *not* appear in the star-chart of C. Bremiker which was then in course of publication from Berlin. Unfortunately the relevant section of the chart had not yet reached Cambridge.

British astronomy was thus robbed of the undivided glory of the first discovery of a heavenly body—or indeed anything else in the physical world—as a result of mathematical prediction. However, it was the Greenwich observations more than anything else that made the achievement possible. Adams concluded his own main published account with a tribute to them, and comments upon their further possible uses. Le Verrier similarly praised 'the scrupulous rigour of the work published by the Greenwich astronomers, work on which the theoretical astronomer can rely with confidence'.

The planet Uranus itself had been the first planet to be 'discovered'—by William Herschel in 1781; it is of interest to note that the first recorded observations were by Flamsteed at Greenwich in 1690, 1712, and 1715 although he did not recognize it as a planet.

A happy note on which to end this section is the fact that in 1847 Airy recommended Adams for the Copley Medal, the highest award at the disposal of the Royal Society; he received it in 1848.

Staff When Pond became Astronomer Royal he had one assistant and no Astronomer Royal before him ever had more; when he retired he had six assistants, but none of these had much standing as a scientist, although in the past history of the Observatory several of the assistants had become men of repute. Airy then insisted upon having a senior assistant, later called chief assistant, who could be accounted an astronomer in his own right and who could deputize for him as necessary. He was fortunate in the three whom he recruited. R. MAIN (1808 – 78) who served 1835 to 1860, when he became Radcliffe Observer at Oxford, E. J. STONE (1831 – 97), chief assistant 1860 to 1870 when he became H.M. Astronomer at the Cape and who succeeded Main at Oxford in 1879, W. H. M. CHRISTIE (1845 – 1922), chief assistant 1870 to 1881 when he succeeded Airy himself. They all became Fellows of the Royal Society and Presidents of the Royal Astronomical Society. They played a leading part in the progress of astronomy in a period that saw a transformation of the whole subject. Each is remembered for a number of individual contributions. As only one example, in 1869 Stone affixed a thermopile at the focus of the Merz telescope and succeeded in measuring the amount of heat received from each of a few of the brightest stars, that from Arcturus seen at an altitude of 25 degrees being about the same as from a 3-inch cube of boiling water at a distance of 400 yards.

JAMES GLAISHER (1809 – 1903) who had been an assistant to Airy in Cambridge was appointed to the Royal Observatory in 1835, and he remained there until he retired in 1874; he was elected FRS in 1849. In many ways he was a more remarkable character than any of the chief assistants. He was a pioneer in meteorological science and the main founder of the Royal Meteorological Society. He was also a pioneer balloonist and on 5 September 1862 he reached an altitude of over 30,000 feet, a height no other man has ever attained without the aid of oxygen. On an ascent in 1863 he observed the solar spectrum at altitudes up to $4\frac{1}{2}$ miles, no comparable feat being performed by any astronomer for nearly a century afterwards.

At the humbler end of the scale, Airy employed computers and the like as and when he needed them. He deliberately kept their remuneration low, since he wished most of them not to hope for a career at the Observatory. But he felt responsibility for their welfare and he made arrangements for their further education while employed in the Observatory.

Records, reports, etc. Airy was meticulous about current and past records. He initiated the Annual Report of the Astronomer Royal to the Board of Visitors, and gave it a form that was followed for almost as long as the Visitors continued to exist. So the progress of the instruments, programmes of observations, research, and so on, may be followed clearly from year to year. He usually concluded the Report with some revealing statements of policy—almost of the philosophy of his administration— or reflections upon trends in astronomy. For instance, in 1873 he conjectured that the time might come when computing would have to be organized on a national basis. Sometimes he inserted matters of general interest as supplementary material in the volumes of *Greenwich Observations* as when in 1862 he gave a concise account of the early history of the Royal Observatory which must have entailed much research of an unaccustomed variety. Airy also took an abiding interest in the Library as a working tool for all members of the Observatory.

Distribution of time Airy saw clearly that the development of travel and communications, as well as many scientific investigations, would demand the countrywide, and later worldwide, distribution of accurate time. As far back as 1849 he seized upon the possibility of exploiting the railway telegraph system—and the fact that certain of its lines ran within half-a-mile of the Observatory enabled him to achieve this in Great Britain in advance of any other country in the world. As a result, in 1880 Greenwich Mean Time was adopted as legal time in this country (and in 1916 in Ireland).

Other investigations and public service To-day time is distributed in a fashion somewhat different from what Airy could have envisaged, but he did start the developments that allow us now to have Greenwich time with incredible precision in our own homes. Moreover we cannot travel by rail or sea, or buy a pound of tea, or pay a gas bill, without being affected by Airy's activities. For he played a leading part in advising industry and the government on the railway gauge, on magnetic compasses in iron ships, on national standard measurements, and on the sale of gas. Airy was also consulted about the construction and operation of the Westminster Clock (often called 'Big Ben' although that name properly belongs to the largest of the associated bells) to such an extent that his own papers on the subject fill three volumes of his records. The fact is that Airy became the national oracle on all technological matters. He also held important public offices, being four times President of the Royal Astronomical Society and the only Astronomer Royal ever to serve as President of the Royal Society, or of the British Association, and he was the first Astronomer Royal to be knighted.

Airy carried out miscellaneous scientific investigations, both theoretical and experimental, each of which was a major undertaking in itself; here are a few examples. He made extensive mathematical studies of wave-optics, and he is remembered for his calculation of the properties of the 'Airy disk', the main part of the irreducible image formed by a telescope of given size. He measured the density of the Earth by comparing the periods of a given pendulum at ground-level and at the bottom of a deep mine. His most famous experiment was that of the water-filled telescope; he repeated the measurement of aberration using a telescope whose tube between the object glass and eyepiece was full of water. Since the speed of light down the tube is then less than in air, a crude interpretation of aberration might suggest that the constant of aberration determined in this way would differ from the standard value. Airy found no detectable difference, and his result is most readily accounted for by the theory of special relativity discovered about 50 years later.

We are however endeavouring to recount the history of the Observatory and not the whole activities of those associated with it and so no more may be included about the awesome range of Airy's service to his age.

Airy's times Airy retired on 15 August 1881, but the following year he was elected a Visitor (which he could not be so long as he was Astronomer Royal) and he attended every Visitation from 1883 to 1891; he died on

2 January 1892. The Observatory has all his official papers, and also a bust of Airy by J. H. Foley (1818 – 74).

When Airy went to the Royal Observatory it had long been a famous place but its work was highly specialized; if the government or the public wanted scientific advice, it went to the Royal Society or to the new specialized societies, and all of them were independent of the government. Under Airy's direction, the Observatory became a great national scientific establishment, small in size by 20th century standards but nevertheless organized along the lines followed by 20th century institutions. And authorities went to it for advice—which meant in practice that they got it mostly from Airy himself. But the principles of state-supported science working for the good of the state, from the germ planted by Charles II in 1675, had thus come to fruition some two centuries later.

Any recollection of Airy's phenomenal outpouring of intellectual energy compels one to wonder as to the driving motivation behind it all. It is difficult to discern anything more than the urge of a man of many talents to exercise them to the full. Airy made no effort to cut a figure on the public stage. But there is little indication that he had any consuming curiosity about the mysteries of the universe that he studied so hard and so long.

Since this book is associated with the Tercentenary, it is interesting to recall Airy's treatment of the Bicentenary. He made no reference to it in his public statements. However in his personal journal he notes '1875 August 10: Dull day, beautiful sunset . . . Held a solemn dinner in the Octagon Room in commemoration of the bicentenary anniversary of the foundation of the Royal Observatory, present Dr Hooker (President of the Royal Society), Professor Adams, Mr Ellery (Melbourne), Mr Russell (Sydney), Mr Stone, the Chiefs of the transit of Venus Expedition, and nearly all the Assistants of the Observatory. August 13 . . . On this day the Observatory Servants and the Workmen had an excursion at my expense to celebrate the Bicentenary Anniversary'. And a distressing feature was that Airy's wife died on 13 August.

W. H. M. Christie

It is a curious paradox that the two Astronomers Royal whose personalities seem most nebulous to us today were those who in many ways introduced the most extensive instrumental innovations. These were Pond and Christie, and our lack of clear pictures of these as individuals is probably due to their coming before and after Airy. He was a more dominating character, but Christie had more sense of direction in astronomical trends. He presided over the greatest enlargement of the Observatory in staff, in territory, in buildings, and in the total light-grasp of its telescopes during the whole of its time at Greenwich.

WILLIAM HENRY MAHONEY CHRISTIE was the first director of the Observatory to have served previously on its staff; he and all his successors (except E. M. Burbidge) were Chief Assistants at some time in their careers. Also he was the first to come of a scientific family. His father S. Hunter Christie and his half-brother J. R. Christie, as well as himself, were Fellows of the Royal Society. They were related to the well-known firm of art-dealers of the same name; they were people of substance, and Christie was a friend of King Edward VII when he was Prince of Wales.

As Chief Assistant from 1870 to 1881, Christie was the pioneer of stellar spectroscopy and photometry at Greenwich, and also of the measurement of polarization of light (from Venus) in astronomy. In 1877 he founded, and edited for several years thereafter, the *Observatory Magazine* which still preserves the form he gave it, so that it remains the most human of all professional scientific journals. Its reports have brought the meetings of the Royal Astronomical Society to life for readers all over the world, many of whom have never actually attended a meeting in their lives.

Instruments   Christie was the first Astronomer Royal who seriously set about equipping the Observatory to observe stars for their own sakes as physical systems. The first requirement for this was a telescope of greater light-gathering power than any the Observatory had ever possessed, and so Christie's first important new instrument was a 28–inch refractor. The glass for the components of the object glass came from the firm of Chance and the object glass and tube were made by the firm of Grubb, these famous names thus first appearing in the annals of the Observatory. In 1894 the new telescope replaced the Merz on the original mounting but with a necessarily enlarged dome, the well-known 'Onion dome'. This fine telescope is now at Greenwich in its original form, under a replica of the original dome (which was irreparably damaged in World War II). This telescope was designed mainly for visual observation because, while it was under construction, Sir Henry Thompson (1820 – 1904), a well-known London surgeon, presented in 1892 a splendid 26–inch refractor designed for photographic work; he followed this by funds for a 30–inch reflecting telescope. These two great instruments were placed on a twin mounting in the dome surmounting the Physical Observatory (see below) and brought into use in 1897 – 8. In modernization of the more traditional work of the Observatory on positional astronomy, Christie early proposed a new altazimuth instrument, which he brought into use about 1898. In 1890 he acquired a 13–inch astrographic refractor.

Buildings   The building originally known as the Physical Observatory—now called the South Building—is the largest in the old Royal Observatory;

it is an impressive specimen of late Victorian construction. It was built piecemeal over the years 1891 – 9 and the tale of labour difficulties, shortage of particular materials, and so on, over this time has a very modern ring. Its construction enabled the growing staff to work under reasonable conditions and it provided improved accommodation for the Library. The central dome now houses the Planetarium of the National Maritime Museum.

In 1897 Christie was granted a new site in Greenwich Park to which to move the Magnetic Observatory away from disturbances on the main site. Unfortunately this soon became liable to far more serious disturbances from electric railways. But this 'Christie Enclosure' served the Observatory well for other purposes during the rest of its time at Greenwich.

Staff At the end of Airy's term the permanent scientific staff consisted of one chief assistant and eight other assistants. Airy employed also non-permanent computers numbering between about 10 and 20. Christie re-formed the establishment and enlarged it so that by 1910 it consisted of two chief assistants, 7 assistants, 11 established computers, with 25 super-numerary computers. A few years after his appointment, Christie was allowed to employ one clerk for office work, the first ever in the history of the Observatory, and he had trouble in finding a suitable man.

Christie recruited brilliant men as Chief Assistants, H. H. TURNER who served from 1884 to 1894, when be became Savilian Professor of Astronomy at Oxford, F. W. DYSON, 1894 – 1906, Astronomer Royal for Scotland 1906 – 10, Astronomer Royal 1910 – 33, P. H. COWELL 1896 – 1910, when he became Superintendent of the Nautical Almanac, A. S. EDDINGTON 1906 – 1913 when he was appointed Plumian Professor of Astronomy at Cambridge.

International cooperation In 1884 by international agreement the Greenwich meridian was adopted as the world's Prime Meridian and the basis of the international Time Zone system.

In 1887 an International Congress on Astronomical Photography, attended by 56 representative astronomers, met in Paris and resolved to make a photographic atlas of the whole sky down to stars of magnitude 14, and therefrom a catalogue of all stars down to magnitude 11. The Royal Observatory was amongst some 18 observatories that undertook to contribute. The work was to be done using specially designed telescopes of 13-inch aperture and $11\frac{1}{4}$-foot focal length. Before Christie's retirement in 1910, the Royal Observatory participants had measured the positions of about 180,000 stars in duplicate, because every star appeared on two plates, and they had counted about 720,000 stars on these plates.

In fact they had finished the Greenwich zone *Catalogue* and *Chart* as its share of the original undertaking; since then later epoch plates have been taken from time to time and much supplementary material on magnitudes, proper motions, etc., has been published. However, the Catalogue as a whole was complete only by about 1958, while the *Astrographic Chart*, as the atlas was called, was actually never finished because it came to be superseded by the *Palomar Sky Survey* 1950 – 7.

Observations and research Under Christie the traditional types of observation were continued with greatly increased efficiency. In addition, the 28-inch equatorial was used for the visual observation of double stars; in one year alone 645 pairs were studied. The Thompson refractor and reflector were used for the photography of stars, comets, satellites and planets. In particular, the last apparition of Halley's comet occurred in 1910 (the next being due in 1986); it was the subject of much calculation before this, and of much observation at the time. On 28 February 1908, using the reflector, P. J. MELOTTE discovered the eighth satellite of Jupiter. Christie led several expeditions to observe total eclipses of the Sun, and he secured fine large-scale photographs of solar prominences and the solar corona in 1898, 1900, and 1905, being thus a chief pioneer of such observations.

The Company of Clockmakers in the City of London dates from 1632, but before Christie the only Astronomer Royal to be admitted was Pond in 1813. Christie was the first to serve as Master, as then did each of his three successors in turn. Christie was knighted in 1904. He was the first Astronomer Royal to retire in accordance with Civil Service rules; this he did in 1910 on reaching the age of 65. He died on 22 January 1922, being buried at sea near Gibraltar.

F. W. Dyson   1910-33

FRANK WATSON DYSON (1868 – 1939) succeeded Christie as Astronomer Royal in 1910. He was a man with great gifts and ample commonsense in using them; he was completely natural and unassuming in all his dealings; he and his family entered much more into the life of the local people than did any of his predecessors; he was a much respected figure in the national scientific community and he was warmly regarded by all who came into personal contact with him. He did much to enhance the national and international standing of the Observatory by greatly encouraging his colleagues to develop independent lines of research of their own choosing. He was one of the most faithful attenders of meetings of the Royal Astronomical Society, where his contributions to discussions gave valued encouragement to young astronomers in particular. The record of achievement at Greenwich during his 22 years as Director is all the more remarkable since after less than four years World War I had started, causing a great depletion of the

PLATE 5

Astronomers Royal

J. Flamsteed 1675–1719

E. Halley 1720–42

Bradley 1742–62

N. Bliss 1762–4

N. Maskelyne 1765–1811

Pond 1811–35

G. B. Airy 1835–81

W. H. M. Christie 1881–1910

W. Dyson 1910–33

H. Spencer Jones 1933–55

R.v.d. R. Woolley 1956–71

PLATE 6

Directors

E. Margaret
Burbidge 1972–3

A. Hunter 1973–5

F. Graham Smith
from 1976

Special occasions

Above:
Annual Visitation 1897

Right:
Royal Visit 1925

PLATE 7

Greenwich

Above: Airy's Altazimuth 1847

Above Right: Great Equatorial 1859

Below: Magnetic Pavilion, about 1890

Right: 'Onion dome' with 28-inch Refractor 1894

PLATE 8

Herstmonceux: Spencer Jones group

Reversible Transit Circle

Photographic Zenith Tube

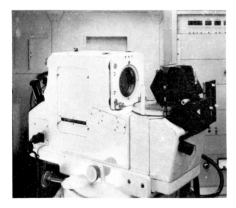

Danjon Astrolabe

Spencer Jones Pavilions

staff – by late 1917 over 30 members were away on War Service – and other disorganization that affected the work until about 1920.

Instruments From August 1911 Airy's reversible zenith telescope was superseded by the Cookson Floating Zenith Telescope on long loan from the Cambridge Observatory. In 1929 G. E. Hale of the Mount Wilson Observatory in California lent a spectrohelioscope for an indefinite period; he had himself invented this instrument, which allows the Sun's disk to be scanned in almost monochromatic light, so that the behaviour of various gases in the Sun's atmosphere may be observed in a comprehensive manner.

In 1931 the Admiralty accepted on behalf of the Observatory an offer by William Johnston Yapp, a well-to-do manufacturer, to provide a 36-inch reflecting telescope together with a dome, for an estimated cost of £15,000. This, the most munificent gift up to that time, was in recognition of Dyson's service as Astonomer Royal from an admirer whom Dyson had never previously met. Yapp stipulated that the instrument should be at Greenwich and so its size was chosen as the largest that could be used productively in the Greenwich climate. It was erected in the Christie enclosure and brought into use in 1934; both at Greenwich and later at Herstmonceux it has proved to be an excellent telescope.

In 1931 the Admiralty agreed to meet the cost of providing a Reversible Transit Circle designed to replace the Airy Transit Circle which had already been in uninterrupted service for 80 years. The new Cooke RTC, as it is usually called, was not erected until 1936, but even then it did not see much regular service until after it was re-erected at Herstmonceux and brought into operation in 1957.

Time and clocks Dyson was much concerned about time-keeping and time-distribution. In 1924 he acquired the Observatory's first Shortt Free-pendulum clock. W. H. Shortt (1882–1971) was a railway engineer; he devised this most accurate of all pendulum clocks in which the only con-nexion between the controlling pendulum and its 'slave' clock mechanism is electromagnetic, and tested it first at the Edinburgh Royal Observatory. It proved so satisfactory at Greenwich that the Observatory used such clocks to maintain Greenwich mean time and sidereal time for about the next 10 years.

In 1924 the Observatory collaborated with the BBC in transmitting the 'six pip' time-signal, which has become such a familiar feature of everyday life and which is still controlled from the RGO. In 1927 the well-known Rugby time-signals were also inaugurated for the benefit of shipping throughout the world. This was the culmination of the Observatory's long striving to provide the mariner with standard time. It should be remarked, too, that ever since signals of this sort have been available they have naturally played a vital part in geodetic measurements, and the Observatory had been the first to exploit this in some very accurate longitude-determinations, as it was later to share in even more precise work making use of signals sent by way of Timation satellite.

Staff Like Christie, Dyson also recruited Chief Assistants who became eminent scientists: S. CHAPMAN 1910 – 1914 and 1916 – 1918 who became one of the world's greatest geophysicists; H. SPENCER JONES 1913 – 1923, H.M. Astronomer at the Cape 1923 – 1933 and Astronomer Royal 1933 – 1955; J. JACKSON 1914 – 1933, when he succeeded Spencer Jones at the Cape; W. M. H. GREAVES 1924 – 1938, Astronomer Royal for Scotland 1938 – 1955.

Observations and research Dyson enlarged the more traditional pursuits of the Observatory in several ways: he introduced the determination of stellar parallaxes by photographic methods; he initiated the systematic determination of stellar magnitudes and colours by photographic photo-metry; in connexion with the Astrographic Catalogue and other surveys, the Observatory carried through various programmes of proper-motion deter-mination, again using photography, and such work led in particular to Eddington's classic studies of star-streaming in the nearer parts of the Galaxy (*Stellar Movements and the Structure of the Universe*, London 1914).

Dyson also did first class work in observing eclipses of the Sun and in organizing British expeditions for this purpose. He saw probably more eclipses than anyone else has ever done. For more often than not the most carefully planned expeditions are frustrated by weather, yet Dyson never had a failure in seven eclipses. At the eclipse of 29 June 1927 in England he helped to organise several novel ventures including the taking of a colour film and the making of photographs from an aircraft. Much of our know-ledge of the outermost parts of the Sun is due to his efforts; the results are summed up in *Eclipses of the Sun and Moon*, Oxford 1937, which he wrote after his retirement in collaboration with R. v. d. R. Woolley.

During Dyson's time the Cookson instrument was engaged on an impor-tant study of latitude variation, or 'wandering' of the poles of the Earth which can amount to 30 feet from the mean position.

Test of relativity In 1916 Einstein published in Germany his theory of general relativity. He propounded three crucial tests which, if successful, would decide in favour of relativity as against classical physics. The most clear-cut of these tests (because the least liable to confusion with other effects) is the 'bending' of light-rays in a gravitational field. In practice, if the theory is correct, this implies that a star seen near the limb of the Sun would appear to be displaced away from the Sun by a definite amount – about one arc-second in feasible cases. The only hope of seeing a star near enough to the Sun is during a total eclipse.

News of Einstein's revolutionary ideas reached war-time England only indirectly. The man who learned most about them was Eddington, who published a report in 1918. But Dyson also realized their profound significance. In a note published in 1917 he discussed the feasibility of the necessary observations, and he pointed out that the eclipse of 29 May 1919 would offer singularly favourable conditions for testing the 'bending' of light. Considering the state of the world in 1918, Dyson and Eddington showed remarkable faith and courage in preparing expeditions, as a joint Greenwich-Cambridge venture, to make the observation. In the event, the expeditions took place successfully, one led by A. C. D. CROMMELIN (Greenwich) to Brazil and one led by Eddington (Cambridge) to Principe off the west coast of Africa. On 6 November 1919, at one of the most historic scientific occasions ever – a joint meeting of the Royal Society and the Royal Astronomical Society presided over by Sir J. J. Thomson – Dyson and Eddington separately demonstrated that the results were in good agreement with Einstein's prediction. Thomson described the prediction as 'part of a whole continent of scientific ideas affecting the most fundamental concepts of physics'.

The first Astronomer Royal made the observations needed to establish that Newton's theory of gravitation gave a good account of natural phenomena; now the ninth Astronomer Royal had organized the observations needed to establish that Einstein's theory gives a better account.

Other Events Dyson's whole tenure was eventful. During the war of 1914 – 18, although as he said the work of the Observatory was 'somewhat curtailed', he did contrive to keep a surprising amount going. The Observatory also undertook additional work with Admiralty chronometers and new work in testing and adjusting more than 3000 binoculars acquired in various ways for the use of the Services. Soon after the War the Observatory joined the rest of the astronomical community in delayed celebrations in 1922 of the centenary of the Royal Astronomical Society; Dyson invited Fellows and Associates to Greenwich on the occasion of that year's Visitation. Then in 1925 the Observatory's celebration of the 250th anniversary of its own founding had as its climax a happy visit on 26 July by KING GEORGE V and QUEEN MARY, the first ever by a Sovereign. The same month the International Astronomical Union met for the first time in England, which meant that Dyson was its chief host. That meeting was in Cambridge, and the next in England was not until 1970 when it met in Sussex near the new home of the Observatory. Dyson became President of the Union 1928 – 32 and he presided over the fourth General Assembly held in 1932 at Cambridge, Massachusetts. He was eager to promote international co-operation in astronomy and in science generally; in 1931 the Observatory played an important part in the international enterprise for observing the minor planet Eros for the re-determination of the Sun's parallax and the mass of the Moon. Nearer home, Dyson always took much interest in the magnetic work of the Observatory and, as will be mentioned below, the Magnetic Observatory moved from Greenwich to Abinger in 1924.

Dyson retired in February 1933; he died on 25 May 1939 on his way home from a visit to Australia and, like his predecessor, he was buried at sea. A portrait by Ernest Moore hangs in Herstmonceux Castle.

War and Peace 1933-55

By the end of Dyson's time, the Royal Observatory had reached the climax of its prosperity at Greenwich. Local conditions and world events were soon to cause the greatest upheavals in its history. But in 1933, with a staff in good fettle and some fine new instruments nearing completion, all seemed to be set fair for Dyson's successor.

Astronomy was poised for great advances, but at the time there was a lull so far as sensational developments were concerned – as there was also in national and international affairs. The previous few years had seen the remarkable successes of theories of stellar structure and the astonishing discovery of the expansion of the universe. Some of the main aims of astronomy clearly were by observation and theory to pursue the consequences of these fundamental achievements. But there were also important technical matters in astronomy calling for attention, as we shall see. Furthermore British and Commonwealth astronomers were soon to start thinking about big instrumental developments in the southern hemisphere.

It was thus a good time for a new director to assume office and to take stock of the situation. And the astronomer best qualified to do this was HAROLD SPENCER JONES (1890 – 1960), a man with abilities as great as any of his predecessors, but probably more scholarly and versatile as a scientist than any of them except Halley, with more awareness of the significance of scientific progress.

As a man, Spencer Jones was richly endowed. He had good looks, dignity and charm, all contributing to a distinquished presence; he was clear and direct in speech and writing, and eloquent when the occasion required it; he was public-spirited and extremely hard-working; in everyday personal dealings he was friendly though shy; in more private life he was relaxed and companionable. As Lord Brabazon said at a memorial service, Spencer Jones was a great man by any standard. But he seemed destined for even greater things than he had opportunity to achieve; for as history turned out he had to spend more energy dismantling instruments than erecting instruments, and more time studying groundplans than studying the heavens. He has, however, left notable permanent memorials in astronomy in general as well as in the development of the Royal Observatory. It was his work more than anyone else's that led to the atom taking the place of the Earth as the astronomer's standard clock; for it was he who in 1939 in a classical paper entitled 'The rotation of the Earth and the secular accelerations of Sun,

Moon and planets' fully established that the Earth's rotation is not quite uniform, and appreciated all the implications of this discovery. And here, by a nice turn of history, he returned to an insight of the first Astronomer Royal who explicitly appreciated that it was necessary to check, as well as might be, whether the Earth's rotation is indeed uniform. Incidentally the group of meridian instruments at the RGO at Herstmonceux has now been very appropriately named the 'Spencer Jones Group' and one of the roads leading to it is 'Flamsteed Road'. (As noted below, after its removal to Sussex, the Observatory was designated the Royal Greenwich Observatory, Herstmonceux, which we may write 'RGO'.)

Instruments Spencer Jones took over responsibility for the construction of the Reversible Transit Circle, to which he gave sustained attention through many years of testing and improving the design. It has now been in continual operation at Herstmonceux since 1957, and has proved to be a splendid instrument. It was at the Royal Observatory where the human element in errors of observation was first systematically taken into account (the 'personal equation') and pioneering work was done in eliminating this element, for example by use from 1915 of the 'impersonal micrometer'. This was carried much further in the development of the RTC; for instance, the settings of the circles are photographed instead of being read by eye, and transit times are automatically recorded on punched cards ready for feeding into a computer.

Spencer Jones also encouraged investigations into the design of other forms of transit instruments in which the sky would be viewed in a movable mirror through a fixed telescope. In particular in 1946 R. d'E. Atkinson proposed the construction of a 'Mirror Transit Circle', and much of it was actually made by the time of his retirement in 1964; tests on the components, so far as they went, appeared to confirm the merits he claimed for it. Unfortunately, this work has remained in abeyance since 1964.

Through the whole history of the Royal Observatory, astronomers have exploited the fact that observations of the highest attainable precision are those made close to the zenith. The US Naval Observatory successfully developed a photographic version of Airy's reflex zenith telescope, and in 1943 Spencer Jones advised the Visitors that an instrument of this sort with a 10-inch objective would be essential for accurate time-determination at the Royal Observatory. The development of this Photographic Zenith Tube (PZT) became a major undertaking of the next dozen years; it was designed by D. S. Perfect of the Observatory and constructed under his supervision by the firm of Grubb Parsons. Ever since it came into operation in 1955 it has been recognized to be the best instrument in the world for its purpose. Copies have been obtained by observatories in Australia and Switzerland.

Like his predecessors, Spencer Jones was much interested in time-distribution; in particular, he cooperated with the Post Office in the installation of the Speaking Clock, and on 24 July 1936 he made the first 'TIM' call, as it was initially. Instead of being still linked directly to the RGO, since December 1964 the Speaking Clock has been checked by the time service equipment at Rugby radio station, whose time signals are in turn monitored at the RGO.

Spencer Jones was more interested than any previous Astronomer Royal, except perhaps Flamsteed, in time-keeping. Here his greatest contribution was the introduction of the quartz crystal oscillator. He installed the first quartz crystal clock at Greenwich in 1938 and, so far as the Time Department was concerned, the change-over from Shortt clocks to quartz clocks was accomplished before the war started in 1939. Post Office (Dollis Hill) standards were used as long-term clocks until 1942. In 1943 quartz clocks were installed at Abinger, to which the Time Department had been evacuated, and thereafter these were used to control the time signals.

On the more workaday level, Spencer Jones began in 1937 greatly to enlarge the repair facilities of the Chronometer Department, and this proved of considerable national importance during the war. Thenceforward he worked much for the re-development of fine watch-making in Britain, and to this end he promoted the foundation of the National College of Horology. From 1939 until his death he was President of the British Horological Institute, and he was Master of the Clockmakers Company in 1949 and 1954. In this connexion it is of interest that the RGO Engineering Workshop foreman, A. C. S. Wescott, constructed the Royal Air Force Memorial Clock in York Minster according to the original design of R. D'E. Atkinson; it was unveiled by the Duke of Edinburgh in 1955.

In view of many technical uses of television in astronomy in recent years, it is noteworthy that as long ago as 1949 A. HUNTER successfully televised the Moon using Royal Observatory eclipse apparatus at Alexandra Palace, while at the beginning of 1954 there was a successful experiment of showing Jupiter and its satellites on television, using the Yapp telescope at Greenwich.

Staff Chief Assistants appointed during Spencer Jones's time were (in addition to the Superintendent of the *Nautical Almanac*) R. V. D. R. WOOLLEY, 1933 – 7, who was afterwards Astronomer Royal 1955 – 71; R. D'E. ATKINSON, 1937 – 64, who was released for war work 1940 – 6; H. R. HULME, 1938 – 45, but he was on war work from 1939 and did not return to the Observatory; T. GOLD, 1952 – 6, who amongst other things for a time extended RGO interests to the monitoring of cosmic rays, particularly those received from the Sun. Thus through the War and until mid-1946 the Astronomer Royal was without a Chief Assistant, and then until 1952 he had only one. From the time when Spencer Jones moved to Herstmonceux in 1948 until the Greenwich site was officially relinquished in 1958, Atkinson up to 1955 and then A. Hunter had immediate charge of activities at Greenwich. The difficulty in finding a new Chief Assistant after the war, though not surprising, was an additional handicap to post-war recovery.

Observations and research Mention has been made of the participation in the observation of the opposition of the minor planet Eros in 1930–1. In 1928 Spencer Jones had been made president of the commission of the International Astronomical Union that was to organize the observational programme with a view to a new determination of the distance of the Sun. Crudely stated, the idea is that if the distance to any member of the Solar System – in this case Eros – can be measured in terms of the diameter of the Earth, then that distance provides a base-line for the triangulation of the rest of the system. The programme was carried out by 24 observatories all over the world which produced nearly 3000 photographs on each of which hundreds of precise measurements had to be made. Spencer Jones himself reduced all the mass of resulting material, a task that took 10 years to complete. This work was the pinnacle of classical astronomy; it was recognized by the award of medals by the Royal Society and the Royal Astronomical Society in 1943. Nearly 20 years later it became possible to establish base-lines by direct measurement by means of radar, thus achieving even higher accuracy.

Other lines of work going on in Dyson's time were mostly continued up to the outbreak of war in 1939. The biggest new development after Spencer Jones took office was the use of the Yapp reflector from early 1934 to take over the work on the colour temperatures of stars organized by W. M. H. Greaves. The whole programme resulted in two volumes *Greenwich colour temperature observations* 1932 and 1952. After the war, the Yapp was brought back into restricted use at Greenwich from 1947.

Because of the war the Airy Transit Circle was out of action from September 1940 until May 1942, but then that stalwart instrument came back again into limited service, being used for observations of Sun, Moon and planets, and of clock and azimuth stars. From 1949–54 it was used as well for a large programme of observation of fundamental stars in readiness for the PZT. It was finally pensioned off on 30 March 1954, and it is now one of the main attractions for visitors to the 'Old Royal Observatory' where it is preserved in working order on its original mounting on the Greenwich Meridian. The Astrographic telescope was also brought back into use at Greenwich after the war for a number of experimental investigations including some on photo-electric guiding. Most of the domes at Greenwich were, however, unusable and there was nothing to be done with other telescopes except to keep them dismounted until the time should come for them to be re-erected at Herstmonceux.

The Magnetic Observatory operated at Abinger without interruption from 1924 to 1957, when it was moved to its present site at Hartland in Devon. The organization of the move was one of Spencer Jones's last duties as Astronomer Royal. He became more concerned not only with terrestrial magnetism but with geophysics generally than any other Astronomer Royal has been. For from 1954 onwards he was much involved in preparations for the International Geophysical Year 1957–8, and afterwards he directed the associated Publications Office to the end of his life.

Nautical Almanac Since 1831 HM Nautical Almanac Office had been an independent Admiralty establishment, but when L. J. Comrie, Superintendent 1930–6, retired the Admiralty placed it under the general direction of the Astronomer Royal. Then in 1949 the Office moved from its wartime quarters in Bath to Herstmonceux, and it became part of the Royal Observatory, the Superintendent ranking as a Chief Assistant. From 1937 to 1971 this was D. H. SADLER, and he was succeeded by G. A. WILKINS. During this interval the means of calculation, the extent of international cooperation, and the forms of publication have undergone enormous transformations. Spencer Jones took a lively interest in the Office and in the wider aspects of its work. He was the Foundation President of the Institute of Navigation 1947–9; D. H. Sadler was President 1953–5. It should also be recalled that during World War II, Sadler organized the Admiralty Computing Service that was the forerunner of most of the large scale computing services in the country, and that itself became the nucleus of the Mathematics Division of the National Physical Laboratory.

Removal Spencer Jones had known Greenwich as Chief Assistant 1913–23 and thereafter he had lived under African skies as HM Astronomer at the Cape 1923–33. On his return to Greenwich he was oppressed by the deterioration in the observing conditions, and almost at once he began thinking about acquiring a better location. As his successor has written, his actions ultimately 'conferred a new lease of life on the Royal Observatory'. Since this outcome was the most important happening for the Observatory after its founding, it seems proper to devote the following chapter to just that part of the history, together with a brief account of the war years with which it happened to be interwoven.

We shall see that in June 1945 the Visitors recommended moving the whole Observatory, except for the magnetic work, to Herstmonceux Castle in Sussex. Naturally, no public announcement could be made for some time.

However, when the war ended in August, most people in the Observatory, although they had never heard of Herstmonceux, supposed that a move would start forthwith – it could take a year or two to get going on the new site wherever that might be, but after that they would be in full enjoyment of the promised land. Alas, however, those six years of damage and dispersal in war were to be followed by ten years of frustration in peace. There was to be a sorry tale of delay after delay caused by shortage upon shortage – of scientists, of materials, of housing, of money – and by recurring economic 'stop-go'. These were the days before 'critical path analysis', but that was not needed in order to demonstrate the homely truth that everything depended upon everything else: instruments could not be moved unless staff could be moved; staff could not be moved without somewhere for them to live; there could be nowhere for staff from London, Bath, etc, to live if there were waiting-lists of local Sussex people needing homes, and so on. By 1945 no new staff had been recruited for over six years; besides the normal wastage, some staff had left for other work and others were not yet released from their war-time employments. Therefore an operation obviously demanding increased manpower had to be embarked upon with an ageing staff below even its pre-war complement. Moreover, all delay meant that any new staff appointed were losing opportunities to learn the work. There is no point here in going into further details, but so much has to be said because Spencer Jones came in for much criticism for not moving more speedily. In retrospect, the wonder is that he preserved not only his sanity but also his equanimity and that he was able at the same time to give close attention to innumerable technical problems about instruments, time-service, and the like. Moreover, it can now be seen that everything Spencer Jones and his colleagues did achieve in the decade after the war was to prove of solid lasting value.

The next chapter will tell how throughout most of the war much of the work of the Observatory had to go into abeyance and much of the remainder had to be dispersed to Abinger, Bath and Bradford-upon-Avon. As we shall also see, however, the Observatory at Greenwich never closed; a small staff carried on there bravely and busily without intermission. Then, as the war drew to its end, the administration returned to Greenwich in July 1945; by October the Astronomer Royal was able to move back into Flamsteed House. Six months later, in April 1946, the Admiralty publicly announced their intention to acquire Herstmonceux Castle and to transfer the Observatory to it, and the operation was set in motion. Some departments then naturally remained in their wartime locations until they could move directly to their new homes at Herstmonceux. The Admiralty completed the purchase in October 1946, and in cooperation with the Astronomer Royal forthwith set to work to plan and effect the adaptation of existing accommodation and to design the development of the whole 370-acre site for all the new buildings that would be required as soon as they could become available.

In skeleton, the narrative of the transfer to Herstmonceux is this:—

In the late summer of 1948 the Astronomer Royal moved into the residence prepared for him in the Castle, the main office there was completed and occupied, the Chronometer Department moved from Somerset to Herstmonceux, and there were preparations for solar work. Incidentally, in the first year the Sun was photographed on 287 days and in 1952 on 311 days, compared with 276 in the last year at Greenwich. In 1948-49 the Hailsham Rural District Council made six houses and, shortly afterwards, several flats available for RGO staff: all along, the Council was as sympathetic and helpful as it could possibly be. The Nautical Almanac Office moved into temporary huts in the Castle grounds late in 1949. The office concerned with the geomagnetic work moved from Greenwich to Herstmonceux in 1950. Although no stellar astronomy had yet started at Herstmonceux, preparations were well under way when a totally unexpected setback occurred: following representations in Parliament about the amenities of the Castle as a national monument, all further building was halted until an architect whose appointment was agreed by the Government and the Fine Arts Commission should have approved plans for all proposed buildings upon the whole site. This added years to the delays and led to the incorporation in the final plans of features that have been perpetual handicaps in operating the site. No significant building work was under way until late 1953. By then also the transfer of the Library to the Great Hall of the Castle was almost complete. At the time of the retirement of Spencer Jones at the end of 1955, the buildings for the Meridian and Equatorial Groups were largely complete and the erection of the meridian instruments was well-advanced. The West Building intended for the Time Department, the Nautical Almanac Office and the Workshops was under way although it was not handed over until January 1958.

International relations The discouragements that beset the move from Greenwich were relieved by many happy features of the post-war years. No British scientist has ever done more for international understanding and cooperation than Spencer Jones. He visited Moscow and Leningrad in June 1945 and in the following years he made several fruitful visits to the US. Also he encouraged visits abroad by members of the RGO staff, and he did much unpublicized work in helping scientists from all over the world to visit this country. He was President of the International Astronomical Union 1945–48, and in 1948 he presided in Zürich over the first General Assembly for a decade. After he retired from the Observatory he served as Secretary General of the International Council of Scientific Unions 1956–58.

While Spencer Jones was the director who removed the Royal Observatory from Greenwich, no one could have greater regard than he had for its historic buildings and instruments. As soon as the move got under way, he began to discuss their preservation with the authorities of the National Maritime Museum. And nothing could be more fortunate than the relevant circumstances. The Museum occupies the beautiful Queen's House and its extensions a few hundred yards from the Observatory across Greenwich Park. It already housed some of the most historic instruments concerned with navigation, some, such as Harrison's chronometer, having been intimately associated with the Observatory. Quite soon it was agreed that the old Royal Observatory should become part of the Museum, housing mainly its own famous instruments but also some others illustrating the development of British astronomy. As early as 1953 the Duke of Edinburgh opened the restored Octagon Room as a notable first stage, and in 1960 Her Majesty the Queen opened the whole of Flamsteed House as part of the Museum. Historians of science, and all who take pride in the long and continuing story of British contributions to fundamental astronomy and its application to human affairs, must be grateful to Spencer Jones for envisaging this memorial and to the Directors of the National Maritime Museum for making it a reality, and to Lt Cdr Derek Howse RN, Head of the Department of Astronomy in the Museum since 1971, who has arranged the display with such consummate scholarly skill.

Spencer Jones retired at the end of 1955. He had been knighted in 1943 and created a KBE in 1955. He died on 3 November 1960.

Renewal

We come now briefly to review the ever-growing difficulties of doing astronomy or geophysics at Greenwich, the damage and disruption and dispersal of wartime, and the commencement thereafter of a new life in a new home.

For almost 250 years the Observatory's activities all flourished within its never more than three acres in Greenwich Park. The first casualty was the continuous recording of the Earth's magnetic field, which had been going on since Airy started photographic recording in 1847. In the days before electric power, Greenwich was as good a place as any for such observations. But the building and later extension of the Deptford and Greenwich Power stations, and the electrification of the South Eastern and Chatham Railway in the early 1920s, finally made it impossible to continue there. No one could tell whether a particular kink in the record denoted activity in the Sun at a distance of 93 million miles, or the passage of a train less than a mile away. So a specially convened meeting of the Board of Visitors in December 1921 told the Admiralty that it was regretfully in favour of moving the magnetic work elsewhere. Possible sites were investigated, the decision to move to Abinger was taken in 1923, and on 6 June 1925 the Visitors met at the Red Lion Hotel in Dorking prior to visiting the new magnetic observatory which was by then in operation. The records show that Dyson and everyone else concerned had handled the matter with thoroughness, determination and expedition, even though there was an interval when the railway authorities tried to apply a remedy themselves. Anyhow we shall see that the Observatory's possession of a base at Abinger was to prove of far greater importance than anybody foresaw in 1925. At the time, however, it was simply a prelude to bigger transformations.

'Observatory Hill (Greenwich) must never be abandoned as the place where fundamental Meridional Observations are to be made' – so wrote Airy in 1861. 'When the Observatory was founded in the golden days of Charles II, Greenwich was a little country town far enough removed from the great capital, and no interference from its smoke and dust had to be feared . . . Now . . . the conditions at Greenwich tend to become steadily less favourable for such work, and it would most probably be found that full efficiency could only be secured by setting up a branch or branches far from the monster town.' That was written by Maunder at the turn of the century and, as a member of the Observatory staff, he was doubtless expressing the accepted view. Even so, 'such work' meant astrophysical observations, and not yet meridian work. Quite soon, however, the Astronomer Royal Christie was telling the Visitors in 1906 that the continued efficiency of the Observatory was seriously threatened by the vibrations and effluents from power stations in the immediate neighbourhood, and he then meant all the work. In particular, the Greenwich L.C.C. Tramway power station half a mile north and actually astride the meridian was an accomplished fact before the astronomers could do much about it. To this day, no one knows how it was possible for this to have come about. When it had happened there was some mild fuss, but they could do little beyond trying to invent mercury pools with maximal damping of oscillations! Indeed it was not until 1934 that action began to be taken about the rapidly increasing atmospheric pollution – the word that was used from the outset. Spencer Jones gave a terse statement of the effects of fine suspended particles and of sulphur dioxide in tarnishing silvered mirrors, contaminating bearings and pivots as well, of course, as contributing along with other industrial effluents to the opaqueness of the atmosphere. He went on to describe the additional troubles caused by modern methods of street-lighting – and so long as astronomical work continued at Greenwich the Borough Council did all they could to minimize these. At the same time, the Observatory started systematic measurements of pollution, and these continued until it finally ceased work at Greenwich. They showed how disastrous the conditions were, but the initial finding that the 'pollution was not on average surpassed by any reporting station in Britain' was slightly affected by the inexperience of astronomers in this type of measurement.

In November 1938 a special meeting of the Visitors at the Royal Society considered a report by the Astronomer Royal regarding 'Removal and future location of certain branches of the work of the Royal Observatory Greenwich'. They reported to the Admiralty that 'it is urgent that the larger astronomical instruments be transferred from Greenwich and a skeleton apparatus for time service be provided upon a site possessing better atmospheric conditions and further that the magnetic observations hitherto carried on at Abinger be transferred to a southern site as far as possible from electrical disturbance' ['southern' because there were magnetic observatories at Eskdalemuir and Lerwick]. This set the business properly in motion. The Visitors held another special meeting in March 1939 and reached two basic conclusions: first, that it was impracticable to find a single site for both astronomical and magnetic work; second, that effort should be made to transfer the whole of the astronomical work to one new site. Thus the view that the Observatory should move as a whole, rather than move certain instruments while keeping Greenwich as headquarters, was reached in peacetime as the considered opinion of the Board – it was not forced upon them by wartime or post-war conditions. Actually there had already been extensive investigation of sites, for the same meeting was fairly clear that the choice of site for the magnetic work was between Lynton and Hartland Point, and that the most favourable site for astronomical work would be found between the South Downs and the sea.

At the Visitation in June 1939 the Admiralty requested more particulars. So the Visitors appointed a Committee composed of Professor E. V. Appleton (later Sir Edward) Chairman, Professor H. H. Plaskett (Oxford), Sir George Simpson, lately Director of the Meteorological Office, Professor F. J. M. Stratton (Cambridge), to carry the investigations further. After consultation with the Astronomer Royal they presented their report the very next month. The statement of the situation concluded with the words 'The bad conditions [at Greenwich] all conspire to prevent the Royal Observatory not only from maintaining its hitherto pre-eminent position in the astronomical world, but even from keeping abreast with other observatories'. Thus they made known the importance of the problem! They proceeded to set out the conditions required to maintain efficiency of astronomical work and of magnetic work. These were both comprehensive and realistic, and they proved to be still all that needed to be said when action could be resumed six years later. For although the Committee and the Civil Engineer-in-Chief at the Admiralty began at once to discuss possible sites, war was clearly imminent by late August; so, no sooner had things got under way than they were forced into abeyance by greater events.

World War II began on 3 September 1939. Almost at once, the Nautical Almanac Office was evacuated to Bath, and the Chronometer Department to Bristol and in 1941 to Bradford-on-Avon. Much of the rest of the work continued at Greenwich until in October 1940 several enemy bombs scored direct hits on the buildings causing damage that was 'though considerable, not serious', in the restrained words of the Astronomer Royal. The place was indeed a sorry sight for years to come. But no major optical component was damaged, for the valuable parts of the instruments had been sent away from Greenwich for safety. Transit observations had continued at Greenwich until September 11/12, 1940; thereafter the emergency stations already organized and equipped with small transit instruments were brought into service. One was at Abinger, and the time-service was operated mainly from there for the rest of the war and until 1957. The other was at the Royal Observatory in Edinburgh, which was always in readiness to keep the service going; as was to be expected, the two Royal Observatories co-operated whole-heartedly. The chief activity being thus at Abinger, and Flamsteed House having been made uninhabitable in any case, the Astronomer Royal made this his headquarters for the rest of the war. Thus, although the quality of Abinger for magnetic observations had already deteriorated, the

Observatory's possession of the site proved to be of major national importance. Spencer Jones recognized then that general research and development had to be postponed indefinitely; at the same time he promised 'a bold policy to make up for stagnation' as soon as conditions would permit.

The Observatory at Greenwich never closed, however. The Solar Department operated throughout the war, and it is their proud record to have photographed the Sun every day it was seen, even if it meant a dash from an air-raid shelter to the telescope and back at the height of a daylight attack. The full programme of meteorological observations was also never allowed to be interrupted. There was in fact no further damage from enemy action until in July 1944 a flying bomb exploded nearby in Greenwich Park, again causing widespread superficial damage to the buildings.

Damage and dispersal served only to spur Spencer Jones to pursue the matter of the move so that everything possible should be ready for action whenever hostilities ceased. In June 1943 he again urged the Admiralty through the Visitors that early consideration be given to the post-war accommodation of the Observatory and its dispersed sections. The circumstances of the time had their compensations in this regard: as well as a good site, a suitable existing building was needed since new building was obviously going to be restricted for a long time, but at that time the Government had particulars of every building of any size, practically every such building in any suitable region was in use for some war purpose that was soon to be finished, and few could revert to their pre-war uses. So it was a time when owners were on the look-out for further users. In fact, it was possible to amass particulars of almost a hundred properties worth considering. Then in February 1944 the Lords Commissioners of the Admiralty replied that they had approved in principle the removal of the Royal Observatory and the Magnetic Observatory to new sites and that, subject to the concurrence of the Treasury, they would seek the approval of the King. All this went on while the country was fighting for its life, and it shows what faith there was in the outcome. Thus encouraged, in June 1944 the Visitors set up a committee consisting of Professor W. M. H. Greaves, Astronomer Royal for Scotland, Professor H. H. Plaskett and Sir George Simpson to consider possible sites for the astronomical work. They went to work with a will, and before the next Visitation they had reduced the list for final consideration first to five and then effectively to two only, Herstmonceux Castle and a site near Andover. In doing this, they had re-affirmed the requirements formulated by the previous committee, along with that for a building that could provide offices, workshops, a refectory, and some living quarters for at any rate the early stages of the move.

The Visitation of 2 June 1945 was again at Dorking, exactly 20 years after the other Dorking meeting, this time at the 'Star and Garter' Hotel. There

Ierstmonceux

otoheliograph

Astrographic 13-inch refractor

inch refractor with Merz guider

Yapp 36-inch reflector

PLATE 10

Herstmonceux: West Building

Nautical Almanac Office, Time
and other departments

Part of Time department

GALAXY measuring machine

Spectrograph made for Anglo-
Australian Telescope

PLATE 11

Herstmonceux: Isaac Newton Telescope

above:

HM The Queen with replica of Newton's reflecting telescope 1671

above right:

HM The Queen with Astronomer Royal at inauguration 1 December 1967

right:

Isaac Newton Telescope

PLATE 12

Royal Greenwich Observatory

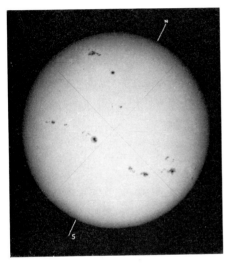

Sunspots 1 April 1958: photoheliograph

Globular cluster of stars M3: INT

Spiral galaxy M51: INT

Irregular galaxy M82: INT

were present Sir Henry Dale, President of the Royal Society, in the Chair, H. H. Plaskett, Sir George Simpson, G. M. B. Dobson, Sir George Thomson, W. M. Smart, W. M. H. Greaves, H. Dingle, W. H. McCrea, F. J. Hargreaves, Rear Admiral A. G. N. Wyatt, C. Jowsey (Secretary) and the Astronomer Royal (Sir Harold Spencer Jones). The Board decided unanimously to approve the committee's report, and to express their preference for the Herstmonceux site.

By the following April the Admiralty had negotiated the purchase of the Castle and 368 acres around it (though the purchase from Sir Paul Latham for £76,000 was not concluded until October 1946 because of the lack of a survey determining the precise boundary of the ground being acquired). Then, with the assent of the King, the Lords Commissioners of the Admiralty formally approved the transfer of the Royal Observatory to Herstmonceux Castle. Subsequently in 1948 they announced: 'Because of the long association of the Royal Observatory with Greenwich since the year 1675, the adoption by international agreement of the Greenwich meridian as the zero of longitude, and the world-wide use of a system of time zones based on that meridian, it was desired to retain the connexion with Greenwich in the new title. The King's pleasure had been taken as to a suitable new title and His Majesty's approval of the designation The Royal Greenwich Observatory, Herstmonceux has been duly signified'.

Sir Roger de Fiennes, Treasurer to the Household of Henry VI, built the Castle about 1446, almost exactly 500 years before the Royal Observatory moved into it. The announcement about it in 1946 said it 'will provide a dignified future home for the Royal Observatory appropriate to its long history and traditions'. The spirit of Sir Christopher Wren, who designed the original observatory 'a little for pompe', was still alive! Actually, the Castle is claimed to be the most beautiful early brick building in the country. Strictly speaking, this applies only to its outer walls, which are protected as an 'ancient monument' and cared for by the Department of the Environment separately from the rest of the building. This circumstance is fortunate since it permits the occupants to do almost what they like with the structure so long as they leave the outside wall intact.

There are interesting coincidences. The original castle at Greenwich on the site of which the old Royal Observatory stands was built at almost exactly the same time as Herstmonceux Castle. Greenwich Park is athwart an old Roman road, and Romano-British remains were found in the Herstmonceux grounds. Airy's interest in tides led him to investigate where the Romans first landed in Britian, and he formed the opinion that it was near Pevensey – only four miles from Herstmonceux. So the great Astronomer Royal who declared that the meridional work should never move away from Greenwich must have come in his explorations close to the place where this work is now done.

Some astronomers hold one view and some another about many matters of policy concerning the national observatory. The debates will continue for as long as there are any astronomers in the land, and a short history is not the place to discuss them. Most astronomers would admit at least that probably no better site could have been found in 1945 or could be found now anywhere in England. It is remarkable that this can be claimed for a place no more than 50-odd miles from London. The expedition and determination with which the business was carried through amidst all the difficulties of the times are to be marvelled at in retrospect. Thus in the first months after the end of World War II (7 May 1945 in Europe, 12 September in Asia) the Observatory was girded for a brave advance into the future.

The previous chapter has shown how sadly the advance was retarded, and how some ten years were spent in the wilderness, but the next chapter will show how nevertheless the promised land came then to be possessed.

Team Work 1956-75

RICHARD VAN DER RIET WOOLLEY (b. 1906) took office as the eleventh Astronomer Royal on 1 January 1956. Like his three immediate predecessors, he had been a Chief Assistant (1933–7), like Dyson and Spencer Jones he came from directing another official observatory (Mt Stromlo Observatory, Canberra, 1939–55), and like Spencer Jones he had an intimate knowledge of the Southern hemisphere (South Africa 1921–6, Australia 1939–55). But he was the first Astronomer Royal to have worked personally with some of the world's largest telescopes, at Mount Wilson, California, 1929–31, and the first to have built up a large modern observatory from almost nothing, as he did at Canberra. The RGO and British astronomy generally was to benefit greatly from the width of this experience. For at Herstmonceux Woolley had in a broad sense to build up a new observatory, to train new astronomers to operate it and to launch a number of these into the world of international astronomy. He threw himself into the undertaking with tremendous vigour and, as a result of his exertions following hard upon those of Spencer Jones, the country has an Observatory that bears a venerable name yet is a great up-to-date research establishment erected upon an ample site that permits the pursuit of many aspects of modern research in astronomy and astrophysics, and that is readily accessible to astronomers from all parts of the United Kingdom.

The review in this chapter, where appropriate, covers developments up to the end of 1974, although Woolley retired at the end of 1971.

Buildings All the patient tenacity of Spencer Jones was bearing fruit at Herstmonceux and at Hartland at the time of his own retirement. All the buildings he had planned were completed in the next couple of years without further serious setbacks, and the temporary wartime huts were demolished in 1957-8. The planning proved to be so generally satisfactory that (apart from the Isaac Newton Telescope which will be dealt with separately) no addition was urgently called for until 1969 when new laboratory and workshop accommodation was added to the West Building. The existing buildings are: (i) *The Castle* which houses the administration offices, the offices of some astronomers, the Library, accommodation for lectures and conferences, the refectory and some living quarters for observers and visitors, the Director's residence; (ii) the buildings for the *Spencer Jones Group* of meridian instruments – mainly 'pavilions' for individual instruments or for their control equipment; (iii) the buildings for the *Group of Equatorial Telescopes* consisting of six main domes together with photographic dark-rooms and the like; (iv) the *Solar Dome* with a large underground space for spectroscopic work, etc.; (v) the *West Building* which houses the Nautical Almanac Office and the Computer-installation, the Time depart ment, offices of the Astrometric and Meridian departments and the GAL-AXY machine, the Archives, and Chronometer room, laboratories and work-shops; (vi) houses for certain maintenance staff.

It may be remarked here that the staff in general live in homes scattered within a radius of some ten miles from the Castle. Since the years when the move to Herstmonceux first began, habits of life have been transformed by the general availability of private cars. In particular, the majority of those on night observing simply drive to and from the Observatory for their hours of duty. There is, however, sleeping accommodation in the Castle that observers may use before or after their night's work.

Much of the Observatory land is let for grazing, and there are also exten-sive plantations that serve to reduce the atmospheric turbulence around the telescopes. These woods and the castle moat and other features provide homes for a great variety of bird-life, which the astronomers are interested in conserving. The exceedingly beautiful walled gardens are open to the public each afternoon in the summer months.

The grounds include also a cricket/hockey field, a tennis court and a club house built by the staff. But even since long before they enjoyed such amenities of their own, the staff have engaged in outdoor games, always with enthusiasm and often with skill–particularly if an astronomer happened to be also an Oxbridge cricket blue. But occasionally there may have been some lack of professionalism as when, at a conference before Woolley's retirement, the RGO played and beat The World at cricket, The World XI being all of international standing – in astronomy, having mostly learned the game of cricket only hours before the match.

Instruments and equipment   In September 1958 Woolley wrote to the Hydrographer of his 'extreme satisfaction in the fact that all the telescopes of the RGO are now mounted and working'. The chief instruments at Herst-monceux in 1974 are:

Spencer Jones group of meridian instruments
PZT, in continuous use since 1957: operation made largely automatic 1961: the probable error in the results of one night's work is estimated to be no more than 3/100 of an arc-second in position and 3/1000 of a second in time: it is used for time-determination and for measuring latitude-variation.

DANJON ASTROLABE, erected 1960, also used for determination of time and of latitude variation.

COOKE RTC in regular use since 1957, chiefly for determining star-positions and planetary positions and motions.

Equatorial group

THOMPSON 30-INCH REFLECTOR: refigured 1960: coudé spectrograph constructed in the workshops and installed 1963: used for stellar spectroscopy with photographic or image-intensifier recording.

YAPP 36-INCH REFLECTOR in operation since 1958 after re-figuring: used for photoelectric photometry, stellar spectrography with image-intensifier spectrograph.

STEAVENSON 30-INCH REFLECTOR presented by W. H. Steavenson to Cape Observatory 1956 and re-figured: returned to RGO 1973: intended for photoelectric photometry.

ASTROGRAPHIC 13-INCH REFRACTOR: now used for photographic determinations of positions and proper motions and stellar photometry, also for monitoring quasars and Seyfert galaxies.

THOMPSON 26-INCH REFRACTOR in regular use at Herstmonceux since 1958 and fitted with auto-guiding system since 1972: used for photographic parallaxes, proper motions, and photometry including monitoring quasar magnitude-variations, and for finding positions of radio sources, and of other objects, eg. artificial satellites and stars that might be occulted by them.

HARGREAVES 38-INCH REFLECTOR, purchased 1972 and under test 1974. This fine telescope was made in England and originally intended for erection at Elisabethville, Katanga, about 1960. It is exceptionally versatile and can be used as a normal reflector at prime, Cassegrain or coudé focus, or else as a Schmidt camera f:3.

Solar group

NEWBEGIN $6\frac{1}{4}$-INCH REFRACTOR presented by A. M. Newbegin 1947, the first major gift to the Observatory at Herstmonceux. Used for observing occultations of stars by the Moon.

PHOTOHELIOGRAPH in daily use since 1949, before which it had been in daily use at Greenwich: attached to the Newbegin telescope: used for daily photograph of the Sun's disk for sunspot record.

SPECTROHELIOSCOPE, on permanent loan from Hale Observatories: used for visual observation of the Sun's disk in monochromatic light (usually the H-alpha hydrogen line) at times of particular activity: allows observer to estimate intensity of a solar flare and velocities of gas therein.

COELOSTAT WITH LYOT FILTER: this combination has been in operation since

1958 and allows a watch to be kept on the Sun in monochromatic light so that activity may be noted and, if required, studied in detail with the spectrohelioscope: Shackman Autocamera also fitted so that an automatic patrol may be operated when needed.

The Newbegin gift included the whole telescope mounting together with its 22-foot dome by Cooke. Therefore all that was needed in order to start solar work at Herstmonceux was a concrete pier to carry the mounting and a simple cylindrical building to carry the dome. It was by having this work carried out by a local builder who happened to have joined the Ministry concerned that it was possible to transfer solar observing to Herstmonceux years ahead of any other sort. The photoheliograph was used at Greenwich for the last time on 2 May 1949, and was slung on the Newbegin to be used at Herstmonceux later the very same day. Most unfortunately, it was the sight of the modest Newbegin dome that so alarmed a local resident as to cause the commotion that led to the reference to the Fine Arts Commission and so to disastrous delays in the rest of the removal to Herstmonceux.

In itself, a telescope is no more than a device for collecting light from whatever source is being studied and focusing as much as possible of the light received as accurately as possible wherever it is needed for investigation. As such, optical telescopes are wonderfully efficient, so that as optical instruments no revolutionary improvement is possible and existing instruments do not soon go out of date. Where development is continually taking place is on the engineering side of mounting and guiding, and on the side of recording and analysing the light. This explains the great importance of an Observatory's engineering workshop and its physical laboratories. Those at the RGO have expanded greatly during the time considered. Cameras, spectrographs, and electronic equipment of all sorts have been developed and constructed for use not only on telescopes at Herstmonceux at the RGO, but also the Radcliffe Telescope, Pretoria, and elsewhere. One of the most exciting developments in recent years has been the use of *image-intensifiers*; the development of one series of such 'tubes' started by J. D. McGee at Imperial College, London has been pursued at the RGO under the direction of D. McMULLAN as Head of the Division of Instrumentation and Engineering, with some highly satisfactory results for the study of the nuclear regions of certain galaxies – to name just one application.

Woolley liked to tell young men that no one should call himself an astronomer who has not watched the Sun come up after a night's observing. No doubt the observer does derive satisfaction from getting the best out of a telescope, the photographic emulsion or other means of recording and the observing conditions generally. This remains largely a matter of personal skill and it has not yet been automated to any great extent. On the other hand, the product of one night's observing can be a few plates that require many days of the most tedious measurement if this is done by conventional methods. Here any possible automation is nothing but welcome. The GALAXY machine – General Automatic Luminosity and XY – the first such machine anywhere, was developed at the Royal Observatory of Edinburgh, and the second one to be constructed was acquired by the RGO in 1972. It does the task as accurately as the best human operative, but with superior consistency and up to one hundred times as fast.

More conventionally as things have now become, the RGO has had a fairly large computer since 1966 and it has been up-graded considerably since then. Besides its primary work for the Nautical Almanac Office it is used for all the computing required in the scientific work of the rest of the establishment.

Shortly after all the existing instruments had been brought into operation, HRH the Duke of Edinburgh spent a day at the Observatory on 14 November 1958. The intention was that he should see the Observatory as it is at work, and he carried this out by a thorough inspection of every department. This exceedingly heartening occasion proved to be much more appropriate than a more formal 'opening'.

Observations and research In the history of the RGO the scope of its scientific work has been expanding all the time with a corresponding growth in staff and with an increasing degree of specialisation in their interests. However, Woolley was the first director to have the resources in scientific manpower and instrumental equipment that called for any significant amount of departmental organization. He and the heads of the main departments formed a team for the general direction of the establishment, and in general each department itself worked as one or more teams. The structure has not been rigid and has evolved over the years: in the sketch that follows it is convenient to take as guide that in operation under Dr Hunter since May 1974. But it should first be stated that the keynote of Woolley's aims was the elucidation of the structure and evolution of the Galaxy, while that of E. M. Burbidge was the behaviour of other galaxies, and that of A. Hunter the future rôle of the RGO in British astronomy generally.

Astrophysics
Woolley organized many visits by himself and his colleagues to do observing runs on large telescopes in California, Egypt, South Africa and Australia, and also to use more modest telescopes in Spain. His own observations were usually for the determination of radial velocities of various classes of stars. At the same time the Department of Astrometry in the RGO since 1961 under the headship of C. A. MURRAY, was busy deter-

mining proper-motions, or transverse velocities, of certain of these stars. From such information got at other observatories as well, Woolley, O. J. Eggen (Chief Assistant 1956-61 and 1964-65 and their collaborators were able to gain new insight into the orbits of stars of various groups about the centre of the Galaxy. Woolley himself also did important theoretical work on the dynamics of these orbits. These investigations could be regarded as an advanced stage of those started at Greenwich almost half a century earlier by A. S. Eddington. Such studies give an indication as to where in the Galaxy certain stars were formed and so they help to elucidate the evolution of the Galaxy. Eggen and D. Lynden-Bell of the RGO and A. R. Sandage of the Hale Observatories in California wrote a very ambitious paper on this subject in 1962 in which they inferred that the Galaxy was formed from a collapsing gas-cloud, the stars of the so-called 'halo' population being formed at an early stage and the 'disk' population, including the spiral arms, in the final stages.

Woolley, R. J. Dickens, Murray, D. H. P. Jones and others in their teams also applied broadly similar methods to the study of particular clusters of stars within the Galaxy, to globular clusters of stars in the outer part of the Galaxy, and to the Magellanic Clouds, our nearest neighbour galaxies. All this work has further advanced the investigation of the evolution of our Galaxy.

B. E. J. PAGEL and his team have been measuring the chemical composition of different groups of stars, using a combination of observational and theoretical methods to study the distribution and history of the chemical elements in the halo and disk of our Galaxy.

In 1969 papers by D. Lynden-Bell served, almost certainly more than any other work, to call attention to the possible widespread importance for astronomy of the gravitationally collapsed objects that have become known as 'black holes'. They are black because effectively no light can escape from such a body; so even if black holes are quite common, it is bound to be difficult to establish their existence observationally. However, in 1971 P. Murdin and B. L. Webster identified the X-ray source known as Cygnus X-1 with a certain star, and from subsequent studies of its velocity-variation they inferred that the star is binary with one component in a highly condensed state. Further work strongly suggested that this is actually a black hole, since a condensed body of the inferred mass would have no option but to form a black hole—unless it happens itself to be a double star. E. N. Walker has collaborated by monitoring the light-variation at Granada University Observatory in Spain. The interpretation of the results remains (1974) in doubt, but the system still offers the most likely candidate for being the first known black hole.

The Observatory's interest in X-ray astronomy has developed rapidly;

much is naturally in collaboration with the groups elsewhere who make the X-ray observations by use of rockets and satellites. A particularly novel exercise on the part of L. V. Morrison was to predict lunar occultations of an X-ray source as seen by an X-ray telescope from the 'Copernicus' satellite in 1973, and then to analyse the results in order to derive an accurate position of the source. Morrison is a member of the Nautical Almanac Office, and this is just one illustration of cross-connections within the RGO, as well as with outside scientists, and thus of the value of a large versatile establishment. The RGO is the only single observatory in the world where such a range of activity is possible.

In 1966 – 67 R. D. Cannon and M. V. Penston who were then research fellows at the RGO and had hitherto been mainly theorists received the Astronomer Royal's approval to observe the quasar 3C 446 which had been reported to be behaving strangely. Their astonishing results were soon confirmed and amplified by comparison with those got independently at two US observatories. Over an interval of several months, the quasar was on average about 20 times as bright as before or since, and was fluctuating so violently that, were it at the distance indicated by its redshift, the variation in the space of a few days was intrinsically equivalent to switching on or off all the stars in the Milky Way. Since then the optical monitoring of quasars and other radio sources has continued at the RGO with important results in classifying the sorts of variation that can occur.

In the years since Woolley promoted visits to other observatories such activities have become ever more frequent; co-operative programmes are now indeed a regular feature. In particular the RGO is engaged in finding accurate positions of radio sources discovered at several radio astronomy centres, using the Isaac Newton Telescope for the optically faintest sources. In fact the first published results from INT observations were 'fundamental' positions of sixteen radio sources of particular interest, or more precisely the optical objects identified with them. In the chain of measurements linking such objects with the positions of fundamental stars, plates taken on the Astrographic telescope provide the first link and those taken on the INT the final link.

Astrometry

The story of the 1919 solar eclipse and the test of general relativity was recalled on page 34. One of the most favourable eclipses for a repetition of the test occurred on June 30 1973 and the University of Texas sent a team to Mauritania for the purpose. B. F. Jones was included, and he brought all the plates obtained to the RGO for measurement on GALAXY.

Since about 1960 the RGO has pioneered modern work on the structure, kinematics and dynamics of stellar clusters, in particular globular clusters for which such work had previously been considered impracticable. More recently it has been able to do more of the near impossible by use of GALAXY. Since stars are almost certainly formed mainly in clusters, this work is essential for understanding the evolution of a galaxy. Again it is work of a sort that can be done only in a large national observatory since it requires the co-operation of several departments extending over many years of observation.

C. A. Murray at the RGO is making a simple but probably unique use of a telescope as large as the Isaac Newton Telescope. This is to measure the parallax of intrinsically very faint stars by taking plates of fields surrounding these stars and measuring them on the forever useful GALAXY. The method has been giving successful results.

Almanacs

The work of the Nautical Almanac Office (NAO) has been mentioned several times, and it is in its own right almost as well known as the RGO itself. There seems to be no doubt that the association of the two has operated for their mutual benefit and for the benefit of astronomy generally. An interesting incidental illustration of this is that the NAO produced charts of the predicted circumstances of a series of occultations in 1974 – 75 by the Moon of the Crab Nebula, which in recent years has proved to be outstandingly one of the most interesting objects in the sky. Amongst many other features, it contains the only known pulsar that can be seen in optical as well as radio frequencies. These occultations should serve to determine very precise positions and extents of various parts of the system.

More generally, the work of the NAO has been entering a new phase of significance. For the use of space probes has led to an upsurge of interest in planetary science which has been nowhere more marked than in Britain, where it is a natural extension of the longstanding vigorous activity in geophysics. This has required new investigations on topics like the dynamics of natural satellite systems which are a development of some of the traditional concerns of the NAO.

Time

Ever since the work of various astronomers culminating in that of Spencer Jones in 1939 showed that the spinning Earth is not the best available time-keeper, astronomers dealing with time have had a triple task: (a) For all purposes not concerned with the rotation of the Earth, they have had to maintain the most accurate possible 'uniform' time (b) For all purposes such as the accurate pointing of astronomical telescopes where the rotation of the Earth is relevant, they have still to maintain the most accurate possible time based upon the rotation of the Earth, i.e. the most refined 'GMT' (c) They must keep the most accurate possible account of the relation between these times. The RGO Time Department, under the headship of H. M. SMITH since 1936, has played a leading part in international co-operation in all these undertakings. Experience having shown that the caesium-beam frequency standard is the best such standard available so far, this was first brought into operational use at the National Physical Laboratory in 1955. The frequency was determined in terms of the best available astronomical time-scale which was that based on the work of H. M. Smith and R. H. Tucker carried out at the RGO in 1953. Since then commercial caesium-beam clocks have been installed at the RGO, six being in operation in 1974; these have long since replaced the quartz clocks which had provided frequency standards between 1938 and 1955. The present installation at the RGO is an important part of the chain of such installations that together since 1968 determine international atomic time (TAI). The RGO has also played a leading part in evolving a system of intercomparison of standards and in publishing the results. The TAI frequency is thus maintained constant to about one part in a million million. Such fantastic precision would delight Flamsteed and would astonish Halley and every one of his successors before Spencer Jones, who was probably the first astronomer to see that it might be possible.

Much of the link-up between atomic and astronomical time depends upon observations made with the PZT. The accuracy of this instrument has proved to be almost unbelievable. Different investigations by D. V. Thomas and by N. P. J. O'Hora have shown that the observations reveal even minute geophysical effects upon the direction of the vertical. Extremely accurate positions and proper motions of the stars that pass near the Herstmonceux zenith are got by repeating the observations in time. They can be got also by repeating the observations at a different station in the same latitude; so in 1968 the Dominion Observatory, Ottawa, installed a second PZT at a site near Calgary; the two are operated in close collaboration.

All this participation in 'fundamental' astronomy naturally involves those concerned in much international consultation in which heavy responsibility rests upon the RGO representatives. It illustrates what so frequently happens in science that when some classical topic seems on the verge of going out-of-date it can suddenly become more vital than ever in connexion with some development in some quite new topic. Thus developments in the study of quasars demand the determination of positions of the optical counterparts with the utmost achievable precision; the study of pulsars and even more recently the study of the constancy of the 'constant' of gravitation, demand determinations of uniform time with all the precision attainable by the means here briefly described; the placing of Mariner 10, in its passage near Mercury in 1974, within 40 miles of the position aimed at was possible only because GMT was available with the required accuracy.

Other work

The foregoing examples of the work can at best convey only its flavour; they are selected quite arbitrarily and the astronomers named are some of the RGO staff who happened to be engaged in the investigations concerned. The magnitude of the work of the RGO as a whole is more difficult to indicate. Some idea may be had from the fact that in 1973 (the year of the last available report), in addition to all the routine publications of the NAO, the Time Department, etc, members of the RGO published in the standard scientific journals over 100 research papers.

This impressive growth in scientific productivity has been achieved without a large increase in scientific manpower. Woolley succeeded in getting it going partly by shedding some long-established commitments. After Abinger had been vacated in 1957 and the magnetic work had been well established at Hartland, Woolley tried for a long time to find an Authority that would more appropriately take responsibility for it. Nothing was achieved, however, until the Natural Environment Research Council (NERC) came into being in 1965, at the same time as the Science Research Council (SRC). In 1967, NERC took control of the Magnetic Observatory; the office concerned with running the Geomagnetism Unit under the management of B. R. LEATON remained happily housed in Herstmonceux Castle, but it was no longer part of the RGO. Then, since the solar work had originally been undertaken in connection with the study of magnetic storms and the like, there ceased to be that particular interest so far as the RGO was concerned. Therefore, Woolley pruned the solar work down to a rather minimal watch upon solar activity, but the international obligations undertaken by the RGO have been conducted efficiently for many years by P. S. LAURIE. Actually the resurgent interest in solar system astronomy may well lead to a renewed interest in the Sun, and the RGO may be one of the few observatories equipped to cope with it.

Mention has been made of the meteorological records maintained at Greenwich. A similar set of records were inaugurated at Herstmonceux in 1952, but Woolley felt impelled to terminate most of the work in 1956.

The responsibility for the Chronometer Department was handed back to the Ministry of Defence (Hydrographer of the Navy) in 1965 but again it remains housed in the RGO. This arrangement has the merit of bringing the Hydrographer to the RGO from time to time and so helping to maintain an association that has been greatly valued for very many years.

Administration As already recorded, from 1675 to 1818 the Observatory was administered by the Board of Ordnance and from 1818 to 1965 by the

Admiralty. Up to 1855, the Astronomer Royal negotiated the conditions of service of himself and his staff directly with these bodies. The Visitors appear to have been consulted about staff less than they were about expenditure on buildings and instruments, although they were kept informed on the subject. Then in 1855 the Civil Service as it is known today was established and the Civil Service Commission was set up. From then until the end of 1945 the staff were in the administrative and clerical grades of the Home Civil Service. The Admiralty, in consultation with the Astronomer Royal, determined the complement of staff, but he was allowed a lump sum within which he could employ temporary supernumerary junior staff, largely as computers. In Airy's time there is occasional mention of a foreman or clerk of works, but otherwise until Christie's time, apart from porters and workmen, all the staff were astronomers or computers with sometimes a skilled mechanic. Christie was the first director to have any clerical assistance in the ordinary business of the Observatory, but it was a long time before he found even one satisfactory clerk. An idea of the administration at the end of last century is given by Christie's report for 1900 in which he states, 'Mr Outhwaite acts as responsible accounts officer; has charge of the library, records, manuscripts, and stores, and conducts the official correspondence . . . The whole number of persons regularly employed at the Observatory is 53.' As in every other establishment, the proportion of administrators has increased considerably throughout the time since that was written. However, it is strange that although the Observatory possesses one of the best astronomical libraries in the world, it has employed a full-time librarian only since 1949; W. P. PRESTON 1949–65, JOAN E. PERRY 1965 – . The Observatory has in recent times been well served by its administrators who have always fully shared the corporate spirit of loyalty of all members; it is sad that space does not permit mention of these many devoted individuals. It is to be noted, too, that the first women computers joined in Christie's time; since then women have occupied positions in the Observatory literally up to the top.

The Scientific Civil Service, as part of the Home Civil Service, was set up from the beginning of 1946. The following year the Treasury agreed that members of the RGO staff should be included in the Scientific Civil Service, but the re-grading and assimilation of staff took about four years, this being another of the post-war pre-occupations of Spencer Jones. He was then able to record, 'The Royal Observatory, the oldest scientific establishment in Great Britain and the one which is best known throughout the world, has thus at last received official recognition as a scientific establishment.'

As will be mentioned in the next chapter, the Science Research Council was set up in 1965, and the RGO forthwith came under its control. At first, the RGO staff were treated as Civil Servants seconded to the SRC. They were allowed in all $2\frac{1}{2}$ years in which to decide whether to transfer to some other employment in the Civil Service or to join the SRC. Almost all did in fact join the SRC. Therein all conditions of service are closely aligned with those of the Civil Service, and recruitment is associated with the Civil Service Commission. But the SRC is legally like any other employer and its employees are not servants of the Crown.

The isolation of an observatory produces its own domestic problems, and no history of the RGO should fail to record the debt that all other members of the staff owe to those who care for the amenities of their working conditions. Amongst those on whom the well-being of British astronomy has depended, as regards both those permanently at work at the RGO and the procession of visiting astronomers and students, over the past quarter of a century, a special niche should be reserved for Mrs E. M. P. Marples who has so long presided over its household affairs.

Students Over the years a number of young astronomers had been welcomed at the Observatory when they came to learn about particular parts of its work. Woolley himself was one of these in 1927. When he became director he organized such visits on a much more regular basis. For about six weeks during every summer since 1956 a group of a dozen or more undergraduate and postgraduate students from universities all over Britain and a few from overseas have been accepted for a Vacation Course. The scheme is financed from government funds and there are corresponding courses at a few other government scientific establishments. But the one at the RGO has a character all its own. Lectures by members of the staff of all departments give the students a conspectus of the work of the Observatory as a whole; each student is attached to a member of the staff who arranges for him or her to share in the work of his team—many a now well-known astronomer's first research publication has originated in this way; everyone is given experience of night-observing at a telescope. The students live in the Castle and, amongst other things, they come to know and value the Library and learn to find their way in current research publications. By now, almost every astronomer in the country, and quite a lot of other scientists, below the age of about 40 is a former Vacation Student of the RGO. They prize not only a unique introduction to professional astronomy but also, many of them, the fact of having played cricket or tennis or piano duets with the Astronomer Royal.

University of Sussex Woolley was intimately concerned with this new university right from the start. He was a member of its preparatory committee and from a very early stage he discussed means of collaboration between the RGO and the University and the possibility of including astronomy among the sciences pursued there. The University received its first students in 1961 and from the start of the session 1965–6, astronomy was recognized as a subject for the Degrees of M.Sc. and D.Phil., Woolley and certain colleagues were appointed as visiting members of the Faculty, and they were giving appropriate lecture-courses at the University. The Astronomy Centre at the University was in being by the beginning of the session 1966–7 and ever since, through cordial collaboration between it and the RGO, it has been recognized as one of the three or four main centres of astronomical teaching and research in the country, and the only one in any of the new universities of the same era. R. v. d. R. Woolley, B. E. J. Pagel, D. Lynden-Bell and E. M. Burbidge have been Visiting Professors, and several other members of the RGO staff have been Visiting Lecturers.

The University part of the Centre has consisted usually of two Professors, one or two other permanent Faculty members, several research Fellows, and visiting astronomers, nearly all of these being concerned mainly with theoretical astronomy. Many of the graduate students are also theorists, but they are all required to have some contact with the observational side, which is obviously to their advantage—an advantage that is almost uniquely available because of the proximity of the Observatory. Those graduate students whose work and interests are mainly observational spend most of their time at the Observatory. One gain to the Observatory is that those of its staff who have not previously had the opportunity to study for a higher degree (M.Sc. or D.Phil.) have since 1966 been able to do so by attending part-time at the Astronomy Centre, and a good many (16 M.Sc. and 5 D.Phil.) have already done this.

Conferences Every spring since 1957 there has been a 'Herstmonceux Conference' on some subject of topical interest related to the work of the Observatory, to which a few leading astronomers in the field from overseas have been invited. These meetings have become a much-valued feature in the calendar of British astronomy.

In 1965 a NATO Summer School on *The kinematical and chemical history of the Galaxy* under the direction of Woolley was also outstandingly successful, and there have been some more specialized conferences from time to time as well.

D. H. Sadler was General Secretary of the International Astronomical Union from 1958 to 1964 so that during those years the Union was operated from the RGO. In August 1970 the 14th General Assembly of the International Astronomical Union met in Brighton and at the University of Sussex. Over 2,000 astronomers and their guests attended the meeting. The RGO received visits on five afternoons and altogether more than 1,000 delegates saw the Observatory in this way.

Staff With the large increase in the number of scientists at the Observatory and the virtual disappearance of the status of Chief Assistant, it becomes invidious to single out individual appointments for special mention. To make exceptions of those appointed after 1950 who left to become directors of other observatories: P. A. WAYMAN who joined the RGO staff in 1951, and in 1957 – 60 was the first member to be seconded to the Cape Observatory, and was head of the Meridian Department 1960–4, became Director of Dunsink Observatory, Ireland, in 1964; T. GOLD, Chief Assistant 1952 – 6, became Director of the Center for Radio-Physics and Space Research, Cornell University in 1959; O. J. EGGEN, Chief Assistant 1956 – 61, 1964 – 5, became Director of the Australian National Observatory, Canberra, in 1965; D. LYNDEN-BELL, head of the Theoretical Astronomy Department 1965 – 72, became Professor of Astrophysics and Director of the Institute of Astronomy, University of Cambridge, in 1972.

Isaac Newton Telescope Since 1967 the largest telescope in operation outside the USA and the USSR has been the Isaac Newton 98-inch reflector (INT) at Herstmonceux (until the Anglo-Australian 150-inch telescope was inaugurated in October 1974). The INT is not part of the RGO, and so the history of its inception, of debates about its location and design, its financial setbacks, and its ultimate construction are not part of the history of the RGO. Nevertheless its history has been closely intertwined with that of the RGO and its existence is obviously of paramount importance to the RGO. The following brief account is confined to aspects in which the RGO has been most concerned.

During 1945–6 there emerged, partly from H. H. Plaskett's Presidential Address to the Royal Astronomical Society, and partly from representations made by Plaskett and Spencer Jones to a committee of the Royal Society, a cogent proposal for a large reflecting telescope for the use of all British astronomers.   According to the records of the time, S. Chapman and W. H. McCrea then independently suggested that the proposal should be linked with the forthcoming celebrations of the tercentenary of the birth of Isaac Newton, who had made the first reflecting telescope. Everyone who was interested acted with such promptitude that on 15 July 1946, the first day of the celebrations, the President of the Royal Society, Sir Robert Robinson, was able to announce that the Chancellor of the Exchequer had agreed to ask Parliament to vote funds for an Observatory with a 100-inch telescope, to be known as the Isaac Newton Telescope, and its ancillary equipment, for the use of astronomers from all observatories in Great Britain. In due course, it was agreed that the Treasury would bear half the capital cost directly, the other half being borne by the Admiralty who were also to bear the upkeep on the Observatory's share of its vote; the INT was to be at

Herstmonceux under the general administration of the Astronomer Royal, though not as part of the RGO. The Royal Society then set up a Board of Management to carry all this into effect.

The project met with friendly encouragement by US astronomers, and when Spencer Jones was in the USA in 1949 he received a letter from Judge H. S. Hulbert to say that the Trustees of the McGregor Fund had agreed unanimously to make an outright gift of a 98-inch glass disk, together with a 26½-inch disk and a plug of glass cut from the large disk in making a central hole (which is always needed in a large reflector). The large disk was of Pyrex cast by the Corning Glass Company in 1936; it was originally intended for use in a telescope for the Michigan University Observatory, but this was never constructed. This noble gift was to the RGO, so that the Astronomer Royal could accept it forthwith, but it was expressly for use in the INT. It gave the scheme a splendid start.

Meanwhile, and for some years more, the Board of Management conducted discussions and investigations of all sorts on proposals for highly novel optical systems, mounting and guiding. Some of the most eminent physicists and engineers as well as astronomers became deeply involved. However, there was no agreement by the time Woolley became Astronomer Royal at the beginning of 1956. As the new Chairman of the Board he soon persuaded them to make up their minds and they decided in favour of a generally orthodox reflecting telescope. A novel feature is its particular corrector lens that greatly improves the field at the prime focus and that was specially designed by C. G. Wynne of the Imperial College of Science.

Apart from delays for financial reasons, the scheme then went steadily ahead. The firm of Grubb Parsons did all the optical work and constructed the mounting and the dome. The Civil Engineer-in-Chief of the Admiralty constructed the building. The telescope was in working order by late 1967.

On December 1 that year Her Majesty the Queen officially inaugurated the Isaac Newton Telescope in the presence of representatives of all who had been concerned in its realization. Afterwards the Queen honoured by Her presence a reception in the Castle ballroom.

In 1965, while the work of erection was in its final stages, the INT became the property of the Science Research Council. It has largely followed the arrangements previously agreed upon with the Admiralty. The RGO maintains the telescope and it has constructed the main accessories in the form of spectrographs and the like, which would be a major undertaking for any observatory. It is estimated that the work being carried out for the INT is equivalent to that of 16 full-time staff. All this service is budgeted for in the SRC support of the RGO. From the start, time on the INT has been allocated by the Large Telescope Users' Panel set up by the SRC under the Chairmanship of the Director of the RGO. This has allocated time also on the Radcliffe telescope in South Africa, and it can arrange for programmes submitted to it to be carried out on smaller SRC telescopes if this is judged to be more appropriate. The RGO astronomers apply for time like anyone else, but in the nature of the case a rather large proportion of the potential users are on the RGO staff. The optical performance of the telescope and all its instruments is fully up to expectations. Its uses include direct and electronographic photography of nebulae, galaxies and quasars, infra-red spectrometry and direct TV scanning of optical spectra.

It is to be remembered that the Royal Society fostered the scheme from the outset. Although it does not now feature directly in the management of the telescope, it does appoint an assessor on the committee of the SRC to which the users' panel reports. So it retains an active interest in what is in fact the national telescope, as it does in the national observatory, having been associated with both throughout their existence.

Achievement The INT has become a familiar feature of the Sussex landscape and to most people it is a pleasing one. It stands as a monument to the exertions of Sir Richard Woolley. In 1956 he took charge of an observatory without a single large telescope in operation, and in little more than a decade not only were all its own telescopes in full operation but also on its site there was the greatest telescope in western Europe. And when he retired from the RGO at the end of 1971 and went to South Africa, astronomy in the southern hemisphere in which Britain has an important share was in a stage of rapid expansion. Certainly he took over at Herstmonceux and in South Africa at propitious times, but certainly also he made the greatest possible use of his opportunities to serve British astronomy. But maybe his most important service has been in inspiring and training the next generation of British astronomers.

Woolley was knighted in 1963; a portrait painted by Margaret Wade in 1971 hangs in the Long Gallery of Herstmonceux Castle.

Moving with the times

Until 1971 Astronomers Royal had held office for an average of nearly 30 years (apart from the one who scarcely entered upon his duties). Presumably no person in authority ever took part in the appointment of more than one, and there never was a recognized routine for this. The Sovereign made the actual appointment, upon advice tendered by the Prime Minister, who in turn had an official recommendation from the Board of Ordnance or the Admiralty. The Government had to rely upon the scientists to guide them, and this can have been only by informal discussion – there is no record to show that either the Royal Society or the Board of Visitors was ever formally consulted. In any case, it is evident in retrospect that on each occasion there happened to be one and only one suitably qualified candidate as regards scientific distinction, age and experience, and administrative ability. Any problem was rather in coming to terms with the obvious man. Furthermore, it was never clear when the title Astronomer Royal became officially attached to the office; it seems that at first it was merely sanctioned by usage.

When the Science Research Council assumed control of the RGO in 1965, as will be related below, it took responsibility for outright appointment of the Director, as for its various other establishments, rather than for simply advising the Government. Although any title of Astronomer Royal could be bestowed only by the Sovereign, when the time came the SRC might have prayed the Sovereign, through the Prime Minister, to bestow it upon the individual appointed as Director. However, before the SRC had published anything about a successor to Sir Richard Woolley, a statement from Downing Street on 22 July 1971 declared that henceforth the two appointments would be made separately. While there was nothing to preclude them going to the same individual, it was clear that this would no longer be regarded as normal practice. In the event, the Prime Minister announced on 27 June 1972 that the Queen had appointed Sir Martin Ryle FRS, Professor of Radio Astronomy in the University of Cambridge, to succeed Sir Richard Woolley as Astronomer Royal. It was understood that there were no duties attached to the office, but that the holder would be available for consultation on scientific matters, and that he should retain the title so long as he remains a professional astronomer within the United Kingdom.

Meantime, in October 1971, the SRC announced the appointment of Dr. E. MARGARET BURBIDGE FRS, as Director following the retirement of

Sir Richard Woolley at the end of the year. She and her husband, Dr G. R. Burbidge FRS, both British born, were professors in the University of California at San Diego, and she was a Vice-President of the American Astronomical Society. She is distinguished for important observational work on galaxies and quasars, and she is the only woman astronomer ever to be elected into the Royal Society. Dr Burbidge took up her appointment in July 1972 on leave of absence from the University of California, but during the ensuing year or so she made several visits on astronomical duties to the USA and two to Australia. During this time she was active in advancing the arrangements for operating the Anglo-Australian telescope; also she began to direct somewhat more of the attention of the RGO towards the astronomy of objects outside the Milky Way Galaxy. However, in October 1973 the SRC announced 'that it had accepted with regret the resignation of Dr E. Margaret Burbidge FRS, as Director of the Royal Greenwich Observatory with effect from 30 November 1973 . . . Dr Burbidge has stated that she prefers to return to her own research work rather than devote a major part of her time to administrative matters. She is returning to her post in the University of California where her husband is also a Professor'.

For the record it must be pointed out that while Dr Burbidge was Director her colleagues relieved her of all detailed administration, in order that she should be free to concentrate her attention upon important scientific matters. They had assured her that they were happy to continue to do this. Thus the 'administrative matters' referred to in the statement, which she feared would occupy a major part of her time had she stayed, could only have been matters of general scientific policy.

'The Council has appointed Dr A. Hunter, the present Deputy Director, as Director with effect from 1.12.73'. This laconic announcement came at the end of the SRC statement. Those few words marked a worthy culmination to a career of distinguished and selfless devotion to the RGO, that thus came to pass as a result of an unexpected turn of history. ALAN HUNTER (b. 1912) had joined the Observatory at Greenwich in 1937, originally as a spectroscopist. During World War II he was seconded for other Admiralty work but returned in 1945. In April 1947 he set out as a member of the British expedition to observe the solar eclipse of May 20 in Brazil. The aircraft carrying Hunter and two colleagues crashed at Dakar; the other two died of their injuries, but Hunter recovered, showing immense courage in overcoming the effects of this experience. He subsequently became expert in other departments of the work of the Observatory: he became a Chief Assistant in 1961 and Deputy Director in 1967, and served as Acting Director for the first half of 1972. In these capacities, and as Joint Secretary of the RGO Committee of the SRC 1965–1973, Hunter had done more than anybody to facilitate the transfer of control from the Admiralty to the SRC, once that step had been decreed by the Act of 1965. Moreover, since he became Acting Director and then Director it has fallen to him to take the lead in discussing with the SRC the future rôle of the RGO in British astronomy as a whole, as will be described below. Also, since long before there was any suggestion that he could ever become Director, he had been the chief planner of the tercentenary celebrations. As it turns out, however, the astronomer who has played a leading part in shaping recent and future history of the Observatory is now the Director who in 1975 presides over the celebration of the whole three centuries of its past.

It was known that Dr Hunter had planned to retire at the end of 1975; in August 1974 the SRC gave the news that F. Graham Smith, Professor of Radio Astronomy in the University of Manchester, was to be appointed Director to take office after Hunter's retirement; from October 1974 he would join the RGO 'at Deputy Director level'. FRANCIS GRAHAM SMITH (b. 1923) is known for important discoveries in radio astronomy; the SRC statement added, 'He has helped to develope radio telescopes and their instrumentation from the earliest postwar designs to the large interferometers and parabolic reflectors in use today'. The RGO being destined for a leading rôle in instrumental development in its own field, and its natural trend being already towards increasing collaboration with astronomers in other fields, Graham Smith's appointment at this juncture is seen as highly appropriate.

The Royal Observatories were the only scientific research establishments supported by the state until the National Physical Laboratory was started in 1900, although state institutions had long employed scientific and technical advice. After that, government support for research grew in many ways under various departments. It became inevitable that a tidying-up operation should sooner or later be called for. This eventually took place when, as a result of the Trend report on civil science, the Science and Technology Act 1965 became law. One result was that the provision for astronomy of all kinds, including optical and radio and, subsequently, infra-red, X-ray, gama-ray and cosmic ray astronomy, whether ground-based or carried out from balloons, rockets or space vehicles, was looked after by the newly established Science Research Council (SRC) on the advice of its Astronomy, Space and Radio Board. This was an advance in that it gave practical recognition to the fact that astronomy is one science, even though it be pursued by different techniques observing in different regions of the electromagnetic spectrum or cosmic ray spectrum. But it is inevitable that each establishment should remain differentiated from others by the special selection of these techniques that it exploits. In particular, the RGO naturally remains a ground-based optical observatory. At the same time, the discoveries made by other techniques exercise a profound influence upon much of the work of optical astronomers – and there is much coming and going amongst astronomers of all branches – even if there is no dramatic change in what an optical observatory looks like from the outside!

An order under the Act of 1965 transferred the RGO together with the Cape Observatory from the Admiralty to the SRC. The Board of Visitors was dissolved by Royal Warrant of 27 August 1965. Its place was to some extent taken by the RGO Committee of the SRC which includes the Hydrographer of the Navy and members nominated by the Royal Society and by the Royal Astronomical Society, as well as some selected by the SRC itself, and unlike the Board of Visitors, the Director is also a member. Each year the RGO prepares its financial estimates in consultation with officials of the SRC; then the RGO Committee discusses them and the scientific policy they are designed to implement, before formally presenting them to the Astronomy, Space and Radio Board. The Chairmen of the RGO Committee have been Professor W. H. McCrea FRS, 1965–71, Sir Martin Ryle FRS, 1971–74, and Professor R. J. Tayler from 1974.

The change of control made little immediate difference to the operation of the RGO, – and this was as intended. The Director and some of his colleagues did indeed find themselves obliged to attend many more committees and consultations in London; this has had some effect in making the work of the Observatory more familiar to other astronomers. On the other hand, the dissolution of the Board of Visitors with its intimate association with the Royal Society has meant that leading British scientists in other fields are no longer induced to concern themselves in the work of this great national scientific foundation. Undoubtedly, this has been a loss to the RGO and, one cannot but suppose, to British science in general.

It was, of course, only natural that there should be no early change in the internal working of the RGO, since any immediately needed reorganization had already been carried through under Woolley's direction and there were well-developed programmes running strongly in all departments; also the Isaac Newton Telescope was nearing completion and the Observatory had a considerable commitment to operate it and develop its instrumentation.

Changes first began to concern, rather, the external relations in regard to astronomy in the southern hemisphere. These had their origins a long way back and only a few salient features may be recalled. In the southern hemisphere astronomers of Argentina, Australia and South Africa had long operated in their own countries. But effectively the only country where astronomers from the northern hemisphere had established observatories was South Africa. British observatories were the Cape Observatory and the Radcliffe Observatory, Pretoria, which had migrated from Oxford in 1935–37; also Armagh Observatory had a share in a telescope at Bloemfontein. The Admiralty had administered the Cape Observatory from its foundation in 1820, and had treated it and the Royal Observatory, Greenwich, as independent establishments. However, there was always much friendly co-operation and many of the Cape staff were recruited from Greenwich. Then in 1959 a process of fusion was initiated; thenceforth astronomers from the RGO have been seconded to the Cape for tours of two years or more, and for a time there was significant secondment in the other direction as well. When the SRC assumed control, it formally recognized the Cape Observatory as a constituent part of the RGO with the Astronomer Royal in overall charge.

The primary commitment of the Cape Observatory, as of the Royal Observatory, has been to 'fundamental' astronomy and, until recent developments took place, it was equipped mainly for such work. The southern hemisphere, however, obviously presents a very rich field for astrophysical observation as well. So it was a momentous step when the Radcliffe Observatory was set up in Pretoria with the purpose of installing a 74-inch reflector, which would then have been, and in due course actually was for some years, the largest telescope by far in that hemisphere. Unfortunately World War II supervened and it was installed only in 1948. Thenceforward it has made tremendous contributions. There was continually growing collaboration with the Cape and through it with the RGO, and, to anticipate a little, in 1967 the SRC entered into a 7-year agreement with the Radcliffe Trust to provide most of the financial support.

In all these ways, and through the participation of Armagh Observatory at Bloemfontein, British astronomers had contributed a major part of what was known about the southern heavens up to quite recent times. After World War II, however, the eyes of other European astonomers turned to the southern hemisphere, where they had hitherto had almost no opportunity to work. Several countries combined to plan a European Southern Observatory, which seemed almost certain to be in Southern Africa. British astronomers too were beginning to desire greater opportunities of this sort and, when their collaboration was sought, they were glad to join in exploring possibilities. However, this particular path to further work in Southern Africa was closed when the Europeans decided to go to South America instead. Then in 1967 the Government of Australia proposed to the British Government that they should contribute equal shares to the construction and operation of a large reflector in Australia. This offered to British astronomers the chance of using a telescope in the southern hemisphere of a size that the United Kingdom could not aspire to secure alone. At the same time observing conditions in Cape Town and Pretoria were deteriorating so as to make it plain that a new site remote from these cities would be needed in any case. Also South African astronomers themselves were interested in the possibility of developing their work in a good location.

Most of those concerned by mutual consent then came to the view that in the short and the long term astronomy would best be served by going ahead with the Anglo-Australian telescope as expeditiously as possible, while looking forward to a time when South African astronomers would by suitable stages take over most of the operation of major facilities in their own country. The SRC therefore instituted a southern hemisphere review in order to work out the best policy and procedure, and they received the report in 1968. As a result they entered into negotiations with South African authorities which led to an agreement for a new South African Astronomical Observatory to replace the Royal Observatory at the Cape from the beginning of 1972. The headquarters are the buildings of the Cape Observatory, but the main telescopes are at Sutherland in the Great Karoo some 175 miles north-east of Cape Town. A United Kingdom financial contribution supports continuing arrangements for United Kingdom astronomers to use the facilities.

Much of the development of the Sutherland installations was supervised by G. A. HARDING of the RGO while serving as Officer-in-charge for the three years 1969–71. Then in January 1972, on retiring from the RGO, Sir Richard Woolley became the first Director of the South African Astronomical Observatory, a happy arrangement that gave satisfaction all round.

To complete this chapter in the story of British astronomical involvement in the southern hemisphere, in 1974 the Radcliffe Trust disposed of the Radcliffe telescope to the South African Government, who plan to re-erect it at Sutherland as part of the South African Astronomical Observatory. That site is apparently proving to be one of the best in the world. Also it should be added that, in shedding responsibilities in South Africa, the RGO did not at the same time assume any share of direct administrative responsibility in regard to the 150-inch Anglo-Australian telescope (or the British-owned 48-inch Schmidt telescope on the same site) at Siding Spring Observatory, NSW, about 200 miles N-NW of Sydney. But the RGO will provide much of the instrumentation.

The RGO has played a vitally important part in southern hemisphere astronomy for over 150 years, by supplying astronomers and instruments, and by consultation and other care for distant colleagues. But it has been only to a minor degree by formal arrangement, and so it has been enormously more than appears from any official records.

In the northern hemisphere astronomical affairs have been progressing along different lines and it now appears that the RGO will be given much more official responsibility, and that this may have some profound effects upon the character of the Observatory itself. But we have to go back to before 1969 to begin this story. British astronomers had for years sought better instrumental and climatic opportunities in the northern as well as the southern hemisphere; some had temporary arrangements for special investigations in many places abroad. In particular, the Astronomer Royal and his colleagues made highly effective use of facilities in California, Egypt, Israel and Spain. As soon as the southern hemisphere review had been completed and accepted, it was therefore inevitable that a northern hemisphere review should be called for. So in January 1969 the SRC set up a committee to review optical astronomy in the northern hemisphere and also to make recommendations about the SRC organization for British optical astronomy as a whole. The review led to further far-reaching examination by the SRC of the parts to be played by its own committees and by the establishments under its control in all branches of astronomy.

This is no place to report such proceedings themselves. But in completing, however, sketchily, the history of the last few years of the three centuries under review certain direct effects upon the RGO have to be recorded. One effect might indeed escape the notice of a later historian (and it makes this historian wonder how many such have escaped his notice!): it is the mundane fact that ever since they began, all these enquiries have been an ever-present pre-occupation for everyone associated with the RGO. While they have been undertaken for no other purpose than increased effectiveness in the future, inevitably they have delayed long-term planning and the start of new enterprises.

A specific matter is that although from the outset all concerned seem to have agreed upon the need for a large telescope, about the size of the Anglo-Australian telescope, in as good a location as possible in the northern hemisphere, there has been endless debate about everything to do with it – whether it should be a British telescope on a site to be shared with others, or whether the aim should be to build up a sizeable British observatory around it, whether a site should be sought in, say, the Mediterranean region, or whether it would be better to go to the other side of the world, whether existing or new establishments should be required to maintain it, and so on. Fortunately, at the time of writing, agreement seems to be emerging on the main issues. That most affecting the RGO is for it to be charged with 'the management of national facilities and the setting up and running of the existing and planned overseas facilities'. The latter are now expected to include a full Northern Hemisphere Observatory for the use of all British optical astronomers. The RGO staff is enthusiastic about this new career. It does indeed mean a new career. Of course, in the foreseeable future the RGO must also play its traditional part in fundamental astronomy. In fact, as recently as 1974 a conference at Herstmonceux of radio and X-ray astronomers along with optical astronomers reaffirmed how vital this work continues to be for *all* astronomers and how there can be no respite in keeping it always up-to-date. The RGO too can still expect to initiate new researches in any branch of astronomy for which it is equipped, although for some while this may have to be in terms of manpower and other resources a relatively restricted part of its total activity. The major responsibility of the RGO is now seen as being to serve the optical astronomers in all British universities and observatories by re-deploying its main forces, with some reinforcement by engineers and others, to produce the chief instruments needed for the great advances expected in the early decades of the fourth century of its existence.

Observatory staff numbers

Director appointed	Scientific and technical	Total
1675 Flamsteed	1	2
1765 Maskelyne	2	3
1881 Christie	10	25
1933 Spencer Jones	41	57
1973 Hunter	136	236

This short table is intended to give a simple picture of the growth of the Observatory. 'Scientific and technical' means established staff in these categories, including the Director. All figures are subject to uncertainty because of unfilled vacancies, etc; in particular, the total for 1881 includes an estimate for supernumerary computers as well as the 'industrial' staff.

Historical Summary and background

Rev Nevil Maskelyne 1765–1811

1766	*Nautical Almanac* starts with issue for 1767
1774	Gravity experiment on Schiehallion
1776 onwards	*Greenwich Observations*
1798, 1805	Bradley's observations published

1771	C. MESSIER: first instalment of catalogue of nebulae and stellar clusters
1781	W. HERSCHEL: planet Uranus discovered
1801	G. PIAZZI: asteroid Ceres discovered
1803/4	W. HERSCHEL: six double stars

John Pond 1811–35

1812	6 ft mural circle by TROUGHTON
1816	10 ft transit telescope by TROUGHTON
1818	Admiralty took control
1821	Observatory in charge of Navy's chronometers
1823	Second mural circle by JONES
1830	Visitors reconstituted
1833	J. POND: catalogue of 1112 stars
1833	Greenwich time ball

1802	W. H. WOLLASTON ⎱ dark lines in
1817	J. FRAUNHOFER ⎰ solar spectrum
1820	Observatory at Cape of Good Hope
1820	Royal Astronomical Society founded
1831	Nautical Almanac Office set up
1833	C. F. GAUSS: *Intensitas vis magneticae terrestris*

Sir George Biddell Airy KCB, 1835–81

1837/8	Magnetic and meteorological observations started
1845	G. B. AIRY: *Reductions of the observations of planets 1750–1830*
1847	Airy's altazimuth telescope
1848	G. B. AIRY: *Lunar Observations 1750–1830*
1851	Airy's transit circle
1852	'Railway time' established
1854	Pendulum experiment at Harton colliery
1859	12¾ inch 'great equatorial' refractor, object glass by MERZ
1873	Solar department started

1834–38	J. HERSCHEL: observations at Cape of Good Hope
1838/9	F. BESSEL, F. STRUVE, T. HENDERSON independently measured stellar parallax
1845	Earl of Rosse: spiral nebulae
1845/6	J. C. ADAMS, U. LE VERRIER independently predict planet Neptune, observed by J. GALLE
1849	A. FIZEAU measured light-speed
1850	W. C. BOND photographed a star
1859	G. KIRCHHOFF and R. BUNSEN initiated spectrum analysis
1873	J. CLERK MAXWELL: *Treastis on Electricity and Magnetism*
1880	GMT became legal time in Great Britain

Sir William Henry Mahoney Christie KCB 1881–1910

1890	13 inch astrographic refractor by GRUBB
1894	28 inch refractor in 'onion' dome
1897/8	Thompson 26 inch refractor and 30 inch reflector erected on twin mounting in Physical Observatory
1898, 1900, 1905	Expeditions to photograph total solar eclipses

1884	Greenwich meridian chosen to be Prime Meridian of the world
1887	Michelson-Morley experiment in Cleveland, Ohio
1887	H. HERTZ: electromagnetic waves
1895	W. K. RONTGEN: X-rays
1897	J. J. THOMPSON: electron
1900	M. PLANCK: light quanta
1905	A. EINSTEIN: special relativity theory
1910	Halley's comet returned

| 1954 | Airy transit circle last used | 1951 | H. I. EWEN and E. M. PURCELL: detected 21 cm radiation |
| 1955 | Photographic zenith tube in use | | |

Sir Richard van der Riet Woolley 1956–71

1956	Atomic frequency-standards adopted	1957	SPUTNIK made first space-flight
1957	Magnetic Observatory moved to Hartland, and transferred to NERC 1967	1957/8	International Geophysical year
		1963	Quasars discovered
		1964	Astronomical X-ray sources discovered
1958	All instruments in operation at Herstmonceux		
1958	Duke of EDINBURGH spent a day at Observatory		
1960	Unification with Cape Observatory initiated		
1960	HM the QUEEN opened Flamsteed House as part of National Maritime Museum		
1964	Computer ICT 1909 installed		
1965	Science Research Council took control	1965	A. A. PENZIAS and W. J. WILSON: microwave background radiation
1966	Sussex University set up Astronomy Centre in collaboration with RGO	1968	Cambridge radio astronomers discovered pulsars
1967	HM the QUEEN inaugurated Isaac Newton Telescope	1969	Men first landed on Moon
1971	Cape observatory passed to South African Astronomical Observatory.	1970	Gamma-ray astronomy developing

Director

Dr Eleanor Margaret Burbidge 1972–3
      Dr Alan HUNTER acting first half of 1972

| 1972 | 38-inch reflector by HARGEAVES |
| 1972 | GALAXY machine |

Dr Alan Hunter 1973–5

| 1974 | Observatory given responsibility for operating projected Northern Hemisphere Observatory | 1974 | MARINER 10 mission to Venus and Mercury |
| 1975 | Tercentenary year | | |

Dr Francis Graham Smith 1976–

Bibliographical Notes

Report of the Astronomer Royal 1836–1964
  issued each year by Royal Observatory
Royal Greenwich Observatory 1965–
  annual report published for each year since 1965 in the *Quarterly Journal* of the
  Royal Astronomical Society; hitherto only summaries had been published by the
  Society.
E. WALTER MAUNDER   *The Royal Observatory, Greenwich.*
  London: Religious Tract Society 1900.
SIR HAROLD SPENCER JONES   *The Royal Observatory, Greenwich.*
  London: Longmans Green 1943, revised 1946.
A. HUNTER   *The Royal Observatory at Herstmonceux.*
  Presidential Address to the British Astronomical Association 1958.
C. A. RONAN   *Their Majesties' Astronomers.*
  London: Bodley Head 1967.
F. BAILY   *An account of the Rev John Flamsteed.*
  London: Admiralty 1835.
C. A. RONAN: *Edmond Halley.*
  London: Macdonald 1970.
WILFRID AIRY (editor)   *Autobiography of Sir George Biddell Airy.*
  Cambridge: University Press 1896.
MARGARET WILSON   *Ninth Astronomer Royal: the life of Frank Watson Dyson.*
  Cambridge: Heffer 1951.
D. H. SADLER   *Man is not lost:* a record of two hundred years of astronomical
  navigation with the *Nautical Almanac 1767–1967.*
  London: HMSO 1968.
P. S. LAURIE   'The Board of Visitors of the Royal Observatory' *Quarterly Journal* of
  the Royal Astronomical Society 7, 169–185, 1967, 8, 334–353, 1968.
P. S. LAURIE   'The buildings and old instruments of the Royal Observatory, Greenwich'
  Observatory 80, 13–22, 1960.
DEREK HOWSE 'The Tompion clocks at Greenwich and the dead-beat escapement'.
  London: reprinted from *Antiquarian Horology* 1970/1.

Much of the present history, brief though it is, is based on unpublished material,
mainly at the Observatory itself, and no published material has been used without
checking it. Under the Public Records Act 1958 the Observatory has been designated
'of national importance' and has been appointed keeper of its own records; since 1958
the archives have been in the charge of P. S. Laurie. No full history of the Observatory
exists. It is understood that a work in three volumes covering the time from the
foundation to 1975 is in active preparation*. This bibliography indicates merely some
further reading in accessible publications. Accounts of most individuals who feature in
the history are in *Dictionary of National Biography*, *Biographical Memoirs of Fellows of
the Royal Society*, etc. There exist in various journals descriptions of the telescopes,
clocks and other equipment; many of the historical accounts, such as the last two items
above, are by P. S. Laurie or D. Howse.

The work carried out at the Observatory in about the first hundred years was
published chiefly in the form of *Observations*, *Catalogues* or *Tables* made by the
Astronomers Royal. Subsequently the Observatory has been responsible for the
official publications of a vast amount of systematic work, besides which much research
work – at present over 100 contributions a year – has appeared in standard scientific
journals; references are supplied in the annual report.

Greenwich Observatory
  Its origins and early development 1675–1835   ERIC G. FORBES.
  Its recent history 1836–1975   A. J. MEADOWS.
  Its buildings and instruments   DEREK HOWSE.